World University Library

The World University Library is an international series of books, each of which has been specially commissioned. The authors are leading scientists and scholars from all over the world who, in an age of increasing specialization, see the need for a broad, up-to-date presentation of their subject. The aim is to provide authoritative introductory books for university students which will be of interest also to the general reader. Publication of the series takes place in Britain, France, Germany, Holland, Italy, Spain, Sweden and the United States.

Wolfgang Wickler

Mimicry
in plants and animals

Translated from the German
by R. D. Martin

World University Library

McGraw-Hill Book Company
New York Toronto

Reprinted 1974
Reprinted 1978

Library of Congress Catalog Card Number 67-26359
Phototypeset by BAS Printers Limited, Wallop, Hampshire, England
Manufactured by LIBREX, Milan, Italy

Contents

Acknowledgments

The following illustrations were prepared by H. Kacher from the following sources (the numbers are figure numbers).
1 after Shelford 1902; 2 after Shelford 1912; 3a after Shelford 1902; 3b after National Geographic *128*, 1965; 4 after Wynne-Edwards 1962; 4a after Animals *8* (12), 1966; 5 after Eisner and Meinwald 1966; 6 two photos from Farbe und Farbenanpassung bei Meertieren; 7 after Bristowe (taken from Wiehle); 8 after National Geographic *128*, 1965, Hinde 1962 and Animals *4*, 1964; 9 after a drawing by Joy Adamson; 10 after Animals *4*, 1964 and author's own material; 11 after Blest 1957; 12 from author's own material; 13 from Proc. Zool. Soc. London 1899; 14 after National Geographic *128*, 1965; 15 and 16 after material from Dr Curio and Dr Longstaff; 17 after Hall, Moreau and Galbraith 1966; 18 after Heikertinger 1954 and Hesse-Doflein 1914; 19 after Hesse-Doflein 1914 and Shelford 1902; 20 after Eisner, Kafatos and Linsley 1962; 21 from author's own material; 22 after Kloft 1959; 23 from various sources; 24 after photos from Mertens; 25 from author's own material; 26 after Gertsch 1947; 28 from the film E 634; 29 after Szidat 1932; 30 from photos taken by Welsch; 31 from author's own material; 32 after Cambridge Phil. Soc. Proc. *10*, 1899; 33 and 34 after various botanical sources; 35 after Bristowe; 36, 37, 38 from material and films by Wickler 1961 and 1963; 39 after Berndt-Meise and from Ottow and Duwe 1965; 40 and 41 from author's own material; 42 from material provided by Dr Nicolai; 43 is a sound spectrograph from Nicolai; 44 after Schwalb 1961; 45 is a photo from Danesch; 46 after various sources and Animals 7, 1965; 47 after Nelson 1964; 48, 49, 50 from material and films by Wickler 1962, 1965; 51 from author's own material; 52 after Kummer.

Introduction

The English naturalist Henry W. Bates spent the years 1849 to 1860 wandering through the forests of Brazil. One of his pursuits was the collection of butterflies, and in 1862, he published his findings in the *Transactions of the Linnean Society, London*. For the next hundred years, the article stimulated heated discussion among scientists, philosophers, theologians, teachers and amateur naturalists. Bates obviously said something which provided a wonderful topic for argument, something of great interest that was difficult to prove or disprove. What did Bates say that was so provocative?

In the course of his eleven years of field research in the Amazon region, Bates captured ninety-four butterfly species, which he classified as Heliconiids. Nowadays, sixty-seven of these species are placed in the Ithomiinae and twenty-seven in the Heliconiinae. As he sorted his catches, Bates grouped those of similar appearance together, as every collector does. But he noticed to his surprise that this gave rise to a number of inconsistencies. Although the butterflies in some of his groups were similar in appearance, some exhibited morphological features which showed that they belonged not just to different species but to different families. One butterfly in particular, *Leptalis* (family Pieridae) showed an especially close resemblance to certain common Heliconiids. Bates wrote 'I have never succeeded in distinguishing *Leptalis* species from the other closely similar species on the wing'.

Bates' article includes two hand-painted colour plates showing Whites (Pieridae) and Heliconiids (Heliconiidae). Curiously, some of the Whites have bright colours resembling those of certain Heliconiids and differ sharply from their next relatives among the Pieridae. Henry Bates was not satisfied with simply shaking his head in amazement at this wonder of nature. Working according to the principle that wonders do not exist, Bates sought an explanation for these unexpected similarities. It is the explanation which he put forward which has aroused interest and opposition ever since.

Bates' argument took roughly the following lines: Heliconiids resemble one another fairly closely, as is to be expected. Some of the Pierids, on the other hand, are distinct from their close relatives.

For these outsiders, there must be some advantage in departing from the norm of the group; they must enjoy a greater chance of survival. An insect, for example, would have a greater chance of survival if it were preyed upon less frequently. Bates, in fact, observed that the Heliconiids were extremely abundant and very conspicuously coloured, and that they also flew amazingly slowly, thus being easy to catch. He noted 'Although they fly slowly and are fragile in construction and apparently have no means of defence, they occur in areas where insectivorous birds hunt in flocks'. The butterflies are apparently not killed by birds, so Bates assumed that the Heliconiids are simply unpalatable, and any edible butterfly which adopts the pretence of being a Heliconiid must enjoy the same protection. This consideration provoked the idea that some Pierids pretend to be Heliconiids and thus enjoy protection which is really deserved only by the unappetising Heliconiids.

When repulsive animals are so conspicuously coloured that they are easily recognised by prospective enemies, the coloration must signify a warning pattern for predators. Once a predator has been convinced of the inedibility of the prey it would probably never again attempt to use it as food. If this is true, then it is possible, or even probable, that an animal which is actually edible and bears a deceptive resemblance to an inedible organism with a warning pattern would also be avoided by the predator. Such unpalatable-appearing and yet edible animals thus possess a false warning pattern, they 'act a part'. An actor is a mime, and so the representation of a false warning pattern was called mimicry. Since Bates was the first to point out this phenomenon, it has received the name *Batesian mimicry* in his honour. Other forms of mimicry also occur, but these will be dealt with later. In general, the animal which is avoided for good reason is called the *model* and the imitating animal is called the *mimic*.

An important concept is contained in the self-evident term 'pattern', or more exactly, warning pattern, camouflage pattern, and protective pattern. Man orients himself mainly with his eyes and he therefore pays particular attention to visual stimuli. But many animals orient predominantly by smell, and our previous discussion of coloration and morphological characters applies equally well to odours (olfactory stimuli). In other words, odours providing a warning effect, camouflage, or mimetic protection must surely exist. The same applies to auditory (acoustical) stimuli. For this reason, it is advisable to refer simply to warning, camouflaging or mimetic stimuli and then specify in each case whether optical, acoustical or olfactory stimuli are involved. Examples will be provided for all of these.

A combination of visible, acoustical and olfactory stimuli sometimes acts to deceive a predator, and the total effect cannot be comprehended if one of these signals is ignored. For example, one case of acoustical mimicry is that of small hole-nesting birds such as tits, especially titmice and chickadees. If such birds are disturbed on the nest, they open the beak, swing slowly from side to side and emit an audible hiss like that of a snake. The loudest component of this hissing noise lies in the frequency range from eight to twelve kilocycles per second, a part of the frequency spectrum to which the human ear is not very sensitive, in contrast to the ears of many other animals. Sibley has assembled a large number of observations on this phenomenon, including some of his own data, and reaches the conclusion that the hiss of a snake represents a case of defensive mimicry. Foraging bumble-bees that spend the night outside the nest and are then unable to fly the next morning because they are covered with dew also hum when threatened. These bumble bees fall on to their backs, perform stinging motions and expel fluid from the anus. Exactly the same behaviour is exhibited by the burying-beetle *Necrophorus investigator* when it is threatened. This insect lies on its back, performs mock stinging motions, although it has no sting at all, expels a stinking, irritant fluid-froth from its anus and hums by scraping the abdomen against the wing-covers.

Proponents of the mimicry theory maintain that any similarity provides at least one of the organisms with an advantage and that the resemblance is therefore useful, or sensible. Certain authors, however, have attacked this view for various reasons. For example, Francé in *Das Leben der Pflanze*, which appeared in 1906, maintained 'that mimicry exists where the resemblance is quite pointless and yet very well developed'. As proof of this, he referred to bryozoans and anthozoans (sea-anemones) mimicking plants, spurges (*Euphorbia* species) mimicking cacti, and marine algae (particularly foliaceous sea-weeds of the genus *Caulerpa*) mimicking ferns, mosses and club-mosses. He also referred to the meadow-saffron (autumn crocus) as a mimic of the crocus, although the resemblance in this case is not so surprising since both are liliaceous plants, and it is a question of taste which plant is regarded as the mimic. Of course, there are many plants which are easily confused, but is this an advantage to one of the plants? Rennet and fool's parsley, for example, look like the hemlock, which is poisonous. If the hemlock were to be avoided by herbivorous animals, then the other plants could enjoy the same protection because of their resemblance to the hemlock.

The difference between pointless and useful resemblances is that in the latter cases there is presumably some other organism which notices the similarity. In addition, it must be important for the attentive organism to recognise the appearance of poisonous plants or animals, since it is advantageous to avoid them. The key figure in all such cases of mimicry is thus the organism which notices the particular character which constitutes the conspicuous similarity between different organisms. We can refer to a character of this type as a *signal*, and the organism reacting to the signal can be neutrally referred to as the *signal-receiver*. The latter is often, but not always, a predator, as will be seen from the examples provided later, so the neutral term signal-receiver is recommended.

Figure 1. Harmless Diptera (flies) are often cited as mimics of poisonous Hymenoptera (wasps, bees, bumble-bees). After several experiences, many birds learn to recognise wasps by their coloration and subsequently avoid both wasps and the similarly coloured flies, although the latter are palatable. The illustration shows wasps (left) and flies (right) from Borneo. Top: *Xylocapa latipes* and *Hyperechia fera*. Middle: *Macromeris violacea* and *Midas n. sp*. Bottom: *Vespa cincta* and *Milesia vespoides*.

1 Batesian mimicry

One hundred years after Bates first clearly defined the concept of mimicry, a review of the literature listed 1,500 papers arguing for or against it. This amounts to roughly fifteen papers a year, or more than one a month. It is thus impossible to survey all the known examples of mimicry, and this would in any case be pointless. Many examples can be found in Cott's *Adaptive Coloration in Animals*. The majority of these examples concern insects, some of which are shown in figures 1–5.

Many insects look like wasps and enjoy the same protection, although they are nothing of the sort. Shelford has provided some interesting examples of this from Borneo. *Xylocapa latipes* is a wasp of quite unusual appearance in that it is squat, lacks a waist and has hairy legs. *Macromeris violacea* is a digger-wasp with long, hairless legs and hunts spiders. Finally, *Vespa cincta* bears a reddish-yellow band around its abdomen and this wasp resembles the wasps with which we are most familiar. All three wasps have a fly species as a double, and these doubles, when active, are not at all easy to distinguish from their wasp partners. *Hyperechia fera* looks like a typical fly, but with *Midas* one has to look a little closer. Wasps have four wings, while flies have only two, their hind-wings having been reduced to halteres. However, the fore-wings of *Midas* are almost as big as the wasp's fore- and hind-wings together. The last mimic, *Milesia vespoides* is even more like a wasp and has yellowish wings like the true wasp (figure 1).

Anyone collecting beetles on the Philippine Islands is in for a few surprises. Lady-birds (Coccinellidae) and leaf-beetles (Chrysomelidae) are typically very conspicuously coloured and there are great differences in coloration from species to species. They are inedible for all insectivorous predators. There is also a large number of Philippine roach species belonging to the genus *Prosoplecta* which behave differently from most roach species. Roaches like to retreat into cracks and fissures, while many tropical species are coloured green like the parts of plants between which they hide. These roaches are readily eaten by insectivorous predators from widely different groups, particularly by lizards. However, the species of

Prosoplecta are not cryptically coloured, nor do they hide in secure retreats; instead they are conspicuously coloured and the genus includes species each of which closely resembles a particular lady-bird species. The roaches can be distinguished by their antennae, which are kept still. Three such species pairs are illustrated in figure 2. In the upper row, a leaf-beetle occuring as two separate morphs is shown together with a roach, the male of which mimics one morph while the female mimics the other. One anatomical peculiarity should be noted: the roaches fly well and have large wings, but the hind-wings are folded together in a special manner. The cutaneous hind part is folded under the tougher anterior part, and in addition the outer margins of both parts of the wing are rolled in when the animal is at rest. By reducing the size of the wings the roach thus simulates the short, rounded form of the lady-bird.

Pherosophus agnathus is a bombardier-beetle which ejects a glandular secretion when disturbed or seized. The fluid burns the fingers and leaves an ineradicable brown spot on paper or cloth. This beetle is extremely conspicuous and has uniformly orange-coloured legs. The grasshopper *Gryllacris* differs from this beetle only in its larger size and in banding of the legs, and both animals occur together in the leafy undergrowth of the jungle.

Tricondyla is a genus of the well-known tiger-beetle family (Cicindelidae). This family is predatory and contains species with a fairly powerful bite, so that they are able to resist small predators. Species of *Tricondyla*, however, are extremely timid and live in the dark jungle. They are very common in Borneo, where several species, differing mainly in size, can be found together. They are found on the jungle floor, where they scurry around between withered leaves and other dead plant material. In exactly the same place can be found the grasshopper *Condylodera tricondyloides*, which resembles the tiger beetles so closely, even in its mode of running, that it was for a long time placed together with the tiger-beetle in Museum collections. R. Shelford, who was the first to compare the animals shown in figure 3, was Curator at the Sarawak

Museum in Borneo. After he had by chance discovered the 'tiger-beetle' grasshopper, he carefully sorted through the tiger-beetle collections in the museum. Shelford did in fact find juvenile grasshoppers of this kind together with tiger-beetle species corresponding in size and finer details of coloration. It must be noted here that beetles pupate and do not alter their size in the adult phase, whereas grasshoppers do not pupate and grow larger through a number of moults.

It is significant that the very young *Condylodera* grasshoppers are not found on the ground but in the flowers of a tree together with the beetle *Collyris sarawakensis* (Cicindelidae), which corresponds in size and in coloration. This grasshopper thus has a number of models with which it may be confused during the course of its life. A somewhat similar phenomenon is found with the praying mantis *Hymenopus bicornis*. The larva looks just like an extremely unpalatable larva of a predatory bug, and is avoided by insectivores, whereas the adult mantis closely resembles a flower (cf. figure 8).

The species illustrated in figure 3a are depicted as they appear pinned out in the museum. A frequent objection to such illustrations is that the relevant similarities are artefacts produced by the process of pinning the insects out in collections. Those who raise this objection usually forget to check whether the author of the publication concerned observed the live animals in their natural habitat. This is in fact not so rare as many opponents of mimicry would like to believe, and for this reason, I have provided illustrations of a living *Tricondyla* beetle and a *Condylodera* grasshopper for comparison. The similarity is if anything greater than that between the dead specimens. One must not forget that large numbers of exceptionally good early colour illustrations of animals, especially insects, were prepared by artists without the aid of colour photographs. The demands of accuracy and time then involved did not permit work in the field and one was forced to rely upon preserved stock. It is nevertheless well known that engravings, frequently hand-coloured, from treatises prepared in the last centuries were often more exact than modern illustrations.

Figure 2. Leaf beetles (Chrysomelidae), with long thick antennae, and lady-bird beetles (Coccinellidae), with short antennae, are protected by unpalatable body juices. They serve as models for roaches (long thin antennae), which are palatable and resemble their models so closely that they are also avoided by predators. Upper row: paired resemblances between the light (left) and dark (right) morphs of the leaf beetle *Oides biplagiata* (Galerucinae) and the light females and dark males of the roach *Prosoplecta trifaria*. The female was originally regarded as a separate species, *P. megaspila*. Lower row: left pair – *Leis dunlopi* and *Prosoplecta semperi*; right pair – *Coelophora formosa* and *Prosoplecta coelophoroides*. All these pairs were trapped at the same site and time of year in the Philippines. The roaches (natural size 9–10 mm) are slightly smaller than the beetles.

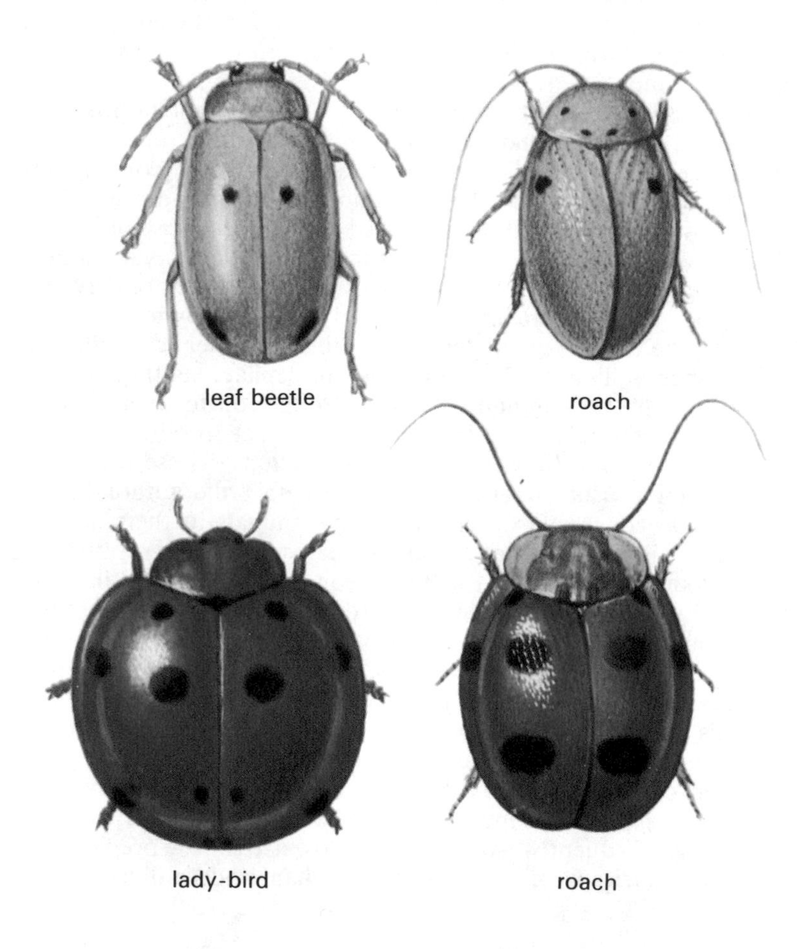

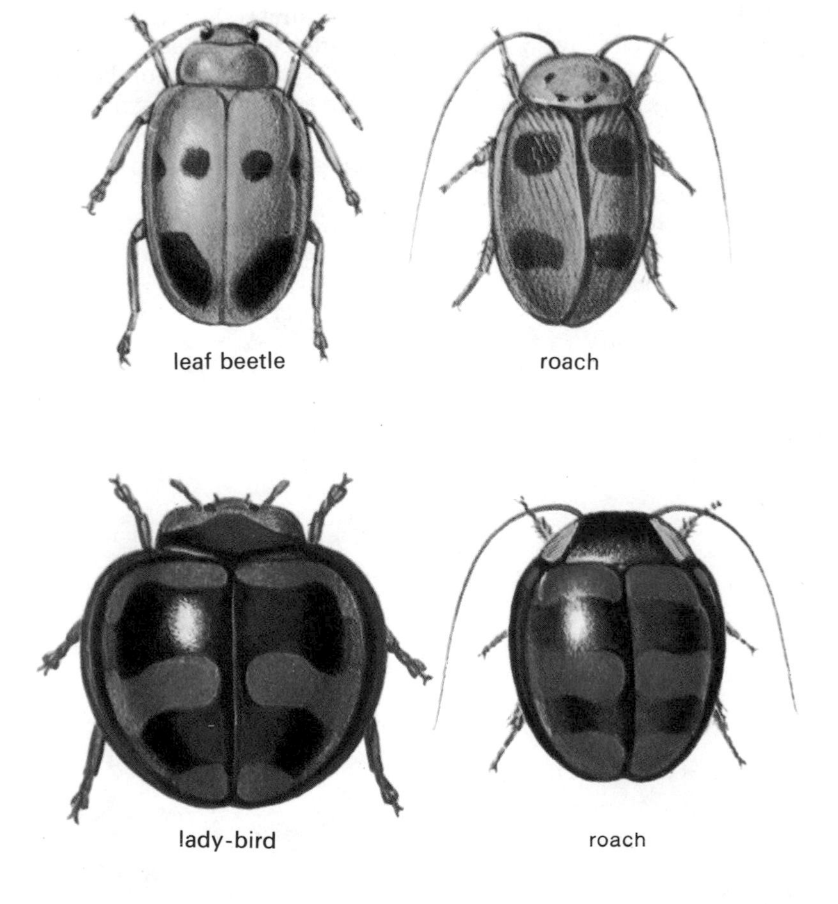
leaf beetle
roach
lady-bird
roach

Examples of mimicry are least common among the vertebrates. The most conspicuous case of apparent mimicry in mammals is described by R. Shelford in *A Naturalist in Borneo* (1916). The well-known tree-shrews (Tupaiidae), which form a systematically isolated group of mammals, are unpalatable. The flesh of these animals has a repulsive taste and it was shunned by all the animals tested, and this probably protects the tree-shrews. Strangely, many tree-shrew species are so similar in appearance to certain palatable squirrel species that skins from the two groups cannot be distinguished without the skull. Shelford names the following mimetic pairs:

Tree-shrews	Squirrels
Tupaia ferrugineus	*Sciurus notatus*
T. minor	*S. jentinki*
T. gracilis	*S. tenius*
T. montana	*S. everetti*
Tana tana	*Funambulus insignis dibersi*

2 Polymorphism in mimetic butterflies

In many cases, a false warning pattern is limited to the female sex of a species. The reasons for this are a matter of debate. On the one hand, butterflies are frequently sexually *dimorphic*, that is, the two sexes are differently coloured. This being so, it must surely be possible for the large variety of colours present in butterflies to be channelled so that the males can also enjoy the benefits of mimicry. On the other hand, it might be more advantageous if the males do not practise mimicry, for then the number of mimics is restricted, which, as we shall see, is an advantage. Finally, it must be remembered that the colours of the male have a signalling significance for the female in the recognition of the sexes, and so cannot be altered. It is nevertheless an indisputable fact that in some butterfly species only the females are protected by mimicry, resembling representatives of other butterfly families. This, for example, is the case with the following families: Papilionidae (swallowtails), genus *Papilio;* Nymphalidae (four-footed butterflies), genera *Hypolimnas*, *Euripus*, *Argynnis;* Pieridae (cabbage-white butterflies), genus *Pareronia;* Acraeidae, genus *Acraea*.

But this is not all. Butterflies that are sexually dimorphic often also show a further distinction of the females into separate types, or *morphs*, and such species are called female-polymorphic. *Polymorphism* is the occurrence together in the same habitat at the same time of two or more distinct forms of a species in such proportions that the rarest of them cannot be maintained merely by recurrent mutation. This is found in the sulphur butterflies (*Colias*, family Pieridae) and the Silver washed fritillary (*Argynnis paphia*, family Nymphalidae). Polymorphic species with mimetic females contain a number of female morphs, each of which has a different model. The most famous examples are found in the genus *Papilio*. The African species *Papilio dardanus*, which Poulton regarded as the most beautiful butterfly in the world, has several female morphs, some of which are not mimics, while others mimic various inedible butterflies (figure 4b). A parallel is provided by the South American *Papilio lysithous* and by *Papilio polytes* in Ceylon. Polymorphism is also found among other insect species, as in the hover-flies.

Figure 3a. The acid-spraying bombardier beetle *Pherosophus agnathus* (top left) is imitated by the adjacent unprotected cricket *Gryllacris sp*.
The protected tiger beetle *Tricondyla gibba* (bottom right) is imitated by the adjacent unprotected grasshopper *Condylodera tricondyloides*. All four are about 2 cm long. *Condylodera* was accidentally discovered in a museum, where it had been included in collections of tiger-beetles.

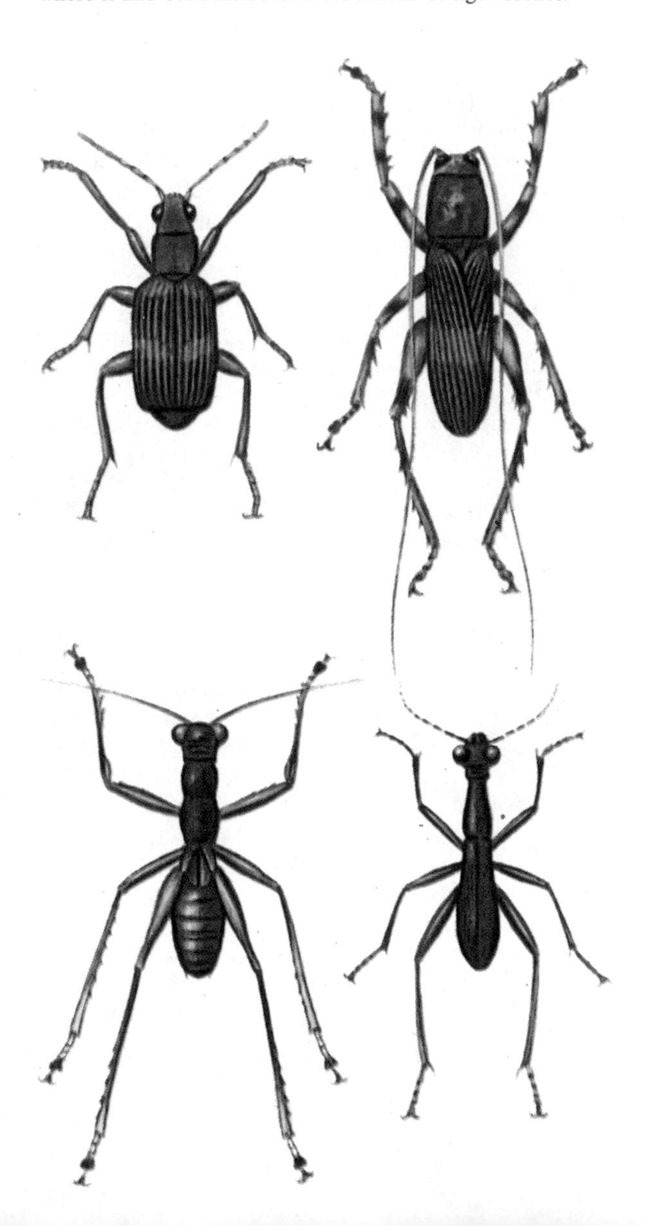

Figure 3b. The similarity in figure 3a is not restricted to museum specimens. The resemblance is just as great in living animals, as shown by the tiger beetle *Tricondyla* (top) and the grasshopper *Condylodera* (bottom).

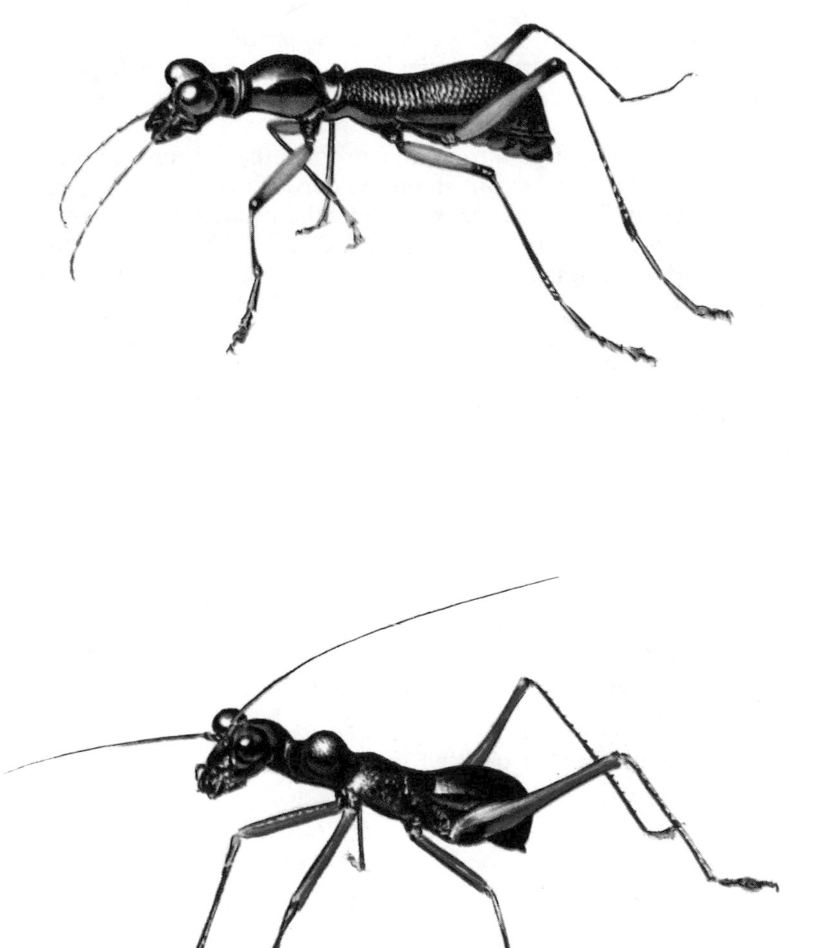

Eristalsis intricarius and *Volucella bombylans*, each of which exhibits different morphs mimicking workers of the small bumble-bees *Bombus terrestris*, *B. agrorum* or *B. lapidarius*. In these cases, however, both sexes are mimics.

All careful investigations of this problem have been confined to anatomical characters. But if the models also show variations in behaviour, it should be expected that the behavioural differences would also be copied by the mimics. Behavioural studies have so far not often been carried out, since this requires more time than a comparison of coloration patterns. Some observations on mimetic behavioural polymorphism have been made, however, for example, on *Hypolimnas dubius* (figure 4b). This species has two morphs—*mima* and *wahlbergi;* the former mimics a number of *Amauris* species (for example, *A. echeria*), while the latter mimics the sub-species *Amauris niavius dominicanus*. The morph *wahlbergi* has a preference for sunlight, exhibits slow gliding flight, rests on the upper sides of leaves and hatches from the pupa in the early morning. The morph *mima* prefers the shade, flies in rapid bursts, rests on the lower sides of leaves and hatches from the pupa in the afternoon. The two morphs, in fact, correspond exactly to their respective models as regards behaviour. G. G. Leigh, who was the first to note these differences, consequently believed that *mima* and *wahlbergi* must be separate species.

The case of *Papilio dardanus*

One of the most astonishing cases of one species resembling another (interspecific resemblance) occurs in a butterfly of the swallowtail family (Papilionidae) in the species *Papilio dardanus*. Unfortunately, this example is very complicated and the general reader may wish to omit the first half of this section.

Papilio dardanus exists in the equatorial zone and adjacent areas, reaching down to South Africa, where it occurs as a number of races of which the females differ greatly in appearance. The males have the appearance that one would expect from a swallowtail butterfly, especially the well-known tail on the hind wings. Some females look like the males, but others can be identified as Papilionids only after careful examination since they look amazingly similar to other butterfly species, always to those which are inedible for insectivorous predators.

The model species belong to the genera *Danaus* and *Amauris* (family Danaidae) whose caterpillars feed on plants with a distasteful milk-sap, especially on milk-weeds and swallow-worts (Asclepiadaceae). The distasteful plant substances make the caterpillars inedible and the inedibility is passed on to the butterfly. Both the caterpillars and the butterflies bear conspicuous warning coloration. The various inedible model species vary in appearance, although the males and females of each species look the same. However, polymorphic species do occur. The following nine races of *Papilio dardanus* are known:

dardanus on the west coast of Africa, from Sierra Leone to Angola
cenea occurring south of *dardanus*
tibullus on the east coast of Limpopo to north of Mombasa
meseres in the vicinity of Lake Victoria and Lake Albert
polytrophus in mountainous areas of Tanzania and Kenya, north east of Lake Victoria
byatti in Somaliland
antinorii in Abyssinia
humbloti on the Comoro islands
meriones on Madagascar

Within these races, polymorphism does occur among the females and each female morph possesses a specific name. None of the female morphs occurs in all of the races. So little is known about the races *byatti* and *humbloti* that they can be set aside, while the race *polytrophus* will be dealt with separately. Since four races possess similar female morphs these will be dealt with as one group.

Figure 4a. The swallow-tail butterfly family (Papilionidae) contains both palatable and unpalatable forms in Malaysia. Caterpillars of the *Atrophanura* species feed on distasteful plants and a poison is transmitted to the butterflies, which are thus unpalatable and protected. *Papilio memnon* caterpillars feed on citrus plants and the butterflies are unprotected. The females of this species differ from the males in appearance and exist as different morphs, each of which resembles a particular unpalatable *Atrophanura* species. In the illustration, the left half of each model is shown with the right half of the slightly larger mimetic morph of *P. memnon*. The tailless form (left) resembles the blue species *Atrophanura nox*, and the tailed form (below) resembles *A. coon*.

The races *dardanus*, *cenea*, *tibullus* and *meseres*

1. The female morph *hippocoonides* (figure 4b, bottom of the middle row) resembles the inedible *Amauris niavius dominicanus*. This latter species is rare in South Africa but common North of the Delgoa Bay, so only 10 per cent of the *cenea* females represent the *hippocoonides* morph, whereas this morph accounts for 85–90 per cent of the *tibullus* females. The *hippocoonides* morph occurs together with *Hypolimnas dubius wahlbergi*, which resembles the same model.
2. The female morph *hippocoon* is common in the range of *dardanus* and *meseres* and resembles a similarly common dark race of the same model, *Amauris niavius*. These forms are accompanied by *Hypolimnas wahlbergi anthedon*.
3. The female morph *trophonius* (figure 4b, second down in the middle row) occurs in the whole of the area so far described alongside the other forms. This morph is rare, however, and only 5 per cent of the females belong to this category, which resembles the model *Danaus chrysippus chrysippus*.
4. The female morph *trophonissa* can barely be distinguished from the morph *trophonius;* it has the same model and occurs on the West coast. Roughly 1 per cent of the females belong to this category.
5. The female morph *cenea* (figure 4b, third down in the middle row) unfortunately bears the same name as a race of the species, which can lead to confusion. This morph resembles a number of closely similar *Amauris* species (*A. echeria*, *A. albimaculata*, *A. crawshayi*). Only 4 per cent or so of the *tibullus* race belong in this category, which includes 85 per cent of the *cenea* race.
6. The female morph *planemoides* (figure 18, bottom of middle row) resembles the inedible *Bematistes poggei* and the males of *B. macarista* (family Acraeidae). This category includes 15–30 per cent of the *meseres* race, but only a small proportion of the *dardanus* race.
7. The female morph *niobe* resembles the inedible *Bematistes tellus*. Both live in the area covering the Cameroons, Angola and the Congo

valley. Only a small percentage of females in the *dardanus* race belong in this category; a very few in fact occur still further North, where *B. tellus* is absent.
In addition, there are a number of other female morphs which are non-mimetic to the extent that no protected models are found in the present range of distribution.

The race *meriones* This race is confined to Madagascar. All the females have the same appearance (they are monomorphic) and also bear a close resemblance to the males, which means that the hind-wings are equipped with a tail. Presumably, this corresponds to the original condition of the species.

The race *antinorii* The females of this race are appreciably different from the other mainland races. Eighty per cent of the females are represented as one morph, which closely resembles the males in appearance. The morph bears a tail, but the fore-wings differ from those of the males in possessing an additional black stripe. A number of other morphs occur alongside this morph, but these other morphs are mimetic despite the fact that they also bear a tail. The commonest of these morphs is *niavioides*, the morph *ruspinae* being relatively rare.

The question arises whether there is any point in speaking of mimicry in the face of this enormous variation within the species. If the wing patterns are so variable, is it not conceivable that one form would resemble another butterfly by coincidence? This can, of course, happen and nobody maintains that the butterfly studies its models and then acquires one or other colour-pattern after mature consideration. All the forms encountered have arisen within the framework of the natural variation of the species. The important thing that must be known is whether more varieties than actually occur could possibly arise and whether any possibilities which are not represented are caused by the lack of a suitable

Figure 4b. Some variations in polymorphism among mimetic butterflies in Africa. Species and morphs from the same area are shown adjacent to one another. Left vertical row: three unpalatable model species, in each of which the males and females look alike; top – *Danaus c. chrysippus* L.; middle – *Amauris crawshayi* Butler; bottom – *Amauris niavius* Trimen. Middle vertical row: various morphs of the mimic *Papilio dardanus*; top – male of the morph *tibullus* Kirby; below – females of the morphs *trophonius* Westwood, *cenea* Stoll and *hippocoonides* Haase (for the morph *planemoides* Trim. see figure 18, bottom of middle row). Right vertical row: other mimetic forms; upper frame – *Hypolimnas misippus* L., in which the female (below) is mimetic while the male (above) is not; lower frame – *Hypolimnas dubius wahlberigi*, in which both males and females are mimetic. The species has different models and occurs as two morphs – *mima* Trimen (above) and *wahlbergi* Wallengren (below). These two morphs also resemble their separate models in behaviour, as explained in the text.

model. Only then is it possible to judge whether the presence of the model has any influence on the frequency and degree of preservation of each variety. The number of possible varieties must be established with breeding experiments, as will be discussed shortly. The relationships of the varieties which occur and the various models can be determined only with experiments in the field, and this has been attempted, with the following results.

It has already been mentioned that the female *hippocoonides* morph shows a regional variation in frequency according to the frequency of the model in each area. This kind of relationship is even more distinct in the range of the race *polytrophus*, for instance in mountainous areas of Nairobi. This area lies between the ranges of the races *meseres* and *tibullus*, which have already been discussed. The models of these two races are almost or completely absent in the mountain range. The race *trophonius* does, in fact, give rise to the morphs previously mentioned, but these are extremely rare among the multitude of other forms, for all of which no model is known to exist even in other areas. In any case, these other morphs exhibit many transitional and intermediate forms. Alongside the reasonably common morph *cenea*, a similar non-mimetic morph *proto-cenea* occurs; *hippocoonides* is accompanied by several varieties of a likewise non-mimetic morph *proto-hippocoonides;* the non-mimetic form *proto-trophonius* (also called *lamborni*) is much more common than the mimetic morph *trophonius*, while both together are much rarer than those forms already named. The morphs *proto-salaami*, *planemoides* and *proto-planemoides* are also found. The prefix *proto-* here denotes that the morph concerned is altered so that the resemblance to the model which it resembles in other areas is lost. Such females sometimes bear indications of a tail on the hind-wings and sometimes carry the characteristic yellow pigment (which fluoresces in ultra-violet light) found in males.

In the area surrounding Nairobi, 133 *Papilio dardanus* females are caught together with 32 model individuals; 32 per cent of the *Papilio* female types have no model. In the area covered by the *meseres* race around Entebbe (in Uganda, on the North shore of Lake Victoria), 111 *Papilio dardanus* females occur alongside 1949 models and only 4 per cent of the females do not fit one or other model. In agreement with this, the non-mimetic female morphs are also more frequent in areas where the model is poorly represented. For example, in places the morph *natalica* represents 10 per cent of the females. This means that the number of *P. dardanus* varieties declines with the number of available models and that the number of non-mimetic forms also diminishes. Carpenter found the same effect with *Pseudacraea eurytus* by comparing the population on Bugalla Island in Lake Victoria with the mainland population. Mimicry collapses in places where models are lacking; so the models do have an effect upon the mimics which resemble them. It has already been stated that this is not an immediate effect, but one which operates indirectly through predators.

The influence of the model on the mimic could operate in one of two ways. Either the predators might eat all non-mimetic butterflies or the non-mimetic forms might not even be produced in areas that are rich in models. The first possibility is improbable, since not all non-mimics are eaten even in areas poor in models. If the second possibility is the correct explanation, then the effect of the model on the mimic should be identifiable in the hereditary make-up of each butterfly.

Polymorphic species are admirable organisms for investigating the inheritance of mimetic characters. Of course, pronunciations about hereditary factors can be made only when the forms under comparison have been crossed experimentally. But this is often impossible, even when the species concerned are quite closely related, and it is naturally impossible with members of different genera, sub-families and so on. But in the case of *Papilio dardanus*, we are dealing with races which can be easily crossed artificially. The offspring of such crosses carry mixed hereditary factors and thus a mixture of observable characters. By means of back-crosses to the two original types, it is possible to emphasise one or other component of the hereditary complement in further generations and thus reach fairly reliable conclusions about the genetical basis of the characters in question. Since so much hypothetical consideration has so far been given to mimicry and its genetical basis, the possibility of finally obtaining results was a very attractive one. It meant collecting various forms of *Papilio dardanus*, which in some cases were extremely scattered, and breeding them for several generations while conducting various crosses. Anybody who has tried to breed butterflies will know just how delicate caterpillars and pupae are and just how stubborn they may sometimes be in their requirements for particular food-plants and cover. In addition, genetical experiments are based upon the proportions between the hybrid butterflies in each generation; so losses in the caterpillar and pupal stages must be reduced to a minimum.

Despite all the expected difficulties, two scientists in Liverpool, C.A.Clarke and P.M.Sheppard, undertook such a study, and their efforts over a number of years proved to be amazingly successful. These two workers took back various races to Liverpool and then bred them. In 1959, Michael Wells conducted an independent expedition on their behalf, travelling from South Africa to Madagascar with the support of the Nuffield Foundation, and collected caterpillars and adult butterflies. Luckily, the caterpillars, which normally feed on citrus plants, also ate the leaves of the Mexican rue *Choisya ternata* with equal relish. This plant is cultivated in England as a garden shrub. It is impossible to explain here in detail the results of the crosses and back-crosses between the various races, nor is it possible to explain exactly how the genetical system operates. Most important are the following results:

1. More female types are obtained than are known in the wild.
2. The coloration patterns, whether mimetic or not, are genetically determined, and the operation of the hereditary factors is dependant upon sex.
3. The tail on the wings is independently genetically determined. (In Abyssinia, there are actually mimetic females with tails, for example *trophonius* or *cenea*.)

4. Externally similar morphs can be developed in different ways genetically, as is the case with the *niobe* variety of *trophonissa* in the West and *salaami* as a variety of *trophonius* in the East.

By far the most important result from these breeding experiments is the proof that mimicry in *Papilio dardanus* cannot be traced to a single gene which retains its effect unaltered. It was shown that there are modifier genes which regulate the function of the genes responsible for the pattern. Such modifier genes can switch the other genes on or off or alter their functional level so as to improve the correspondence of the mimic with the model; furthermore, they reduce the range of variation to a restricted number of mimetic forms. But the effect of modifier genes from one race is not carried over in crosses with another. This means that these genes are apparently adapted to the gene complex with which they normally occur and were probably developed simultaneously. This mutual adaptation of different genes within the gene complex, which restricts variability and thus enhances the mimetic effect, represents the influence of the model on the mimic which was suggested previously.

The investigation carried out by Clark and Sheppard has, in this one case, decisively shown which of the various ways postulated has actually been used in the evolution of mimicry. Other similar investigations have since been carried out, and all lead to the conclusion that mimics do not suddenly appear ready-made. If a chance mutation within an unprotected species should happen to produce a degree of similarity to a protected species, the gene gradually spreads through the population because of its advantageous effect. During this process, the operation of the gene gradually undergoes modification so that the mimetic similarity which it promotes is improved.

Mating, polymorphism and mimicry

In polymorphic species where conspecifics (members of the same species) may be quite different in appearance, and in the converse case where mimics closely resemble members of another species, it might be imagined that confusion arises in mating. As already mentioned, the male of a mimetic butterfly species is often conservative in its coloration and thus resembles related species; only the female departs from the typical pattern and resembles an unrelated species. It has been shown in genetical experiments that this is not due to a greater variability of the female genes. As early as 1874, Belt, who had travelled extensively in Nicaragua, assumed that the females were the cause of male conservatism because they selected conservative males during pair-formation. This would mean that the females recognise the males largely by visual means. Recently, behavourists have tried to test this assumption, but there is still no satisfactory explanation for the non-mimetic appearance of the males. A few facts have been gleaned, however, and these will be discussed briefly.

In order for sex recognition in animals to be possible, at least one of the partners must be able to distinguish conspecifics from other species and males from females. This requires sensory organs and signals. In other words, the animal must be capable of sight, hearing, touch and/or the chemical sense of taste and smell. It is always important to establish which senses are employed in each case, and Professor Magnus has carried out experiments on this in the wild with the Silver washed fritillary *Argynnis paphia*. The males of this butterfly either sit and wait for females or search for them with a characteristic zig-zag flight. They approach any object which looks and moves like a female. Both males and females are yellow-brown dorsally and dark ventrally; the two sides are seen alternately during flight. Magnus carried out his experiments with a specially-constructed roundabout in woodland glades. The machine bore two long arms, each carrying a model whose size, colour and wing-beat frequency could be varied. The models appeared to fly when the roundabout was set in motion. A very effective model was a horizontally mounted cylinder with alternating dark and light stripes, which could be rotated to imitate the dark-light effect of a flying female. It was shown that oversize models were more effective than normally sized ones, and that the effectiveness increased with the speed of light-dark alternation. This increase with speed continued as long as the male eye could distinguish the black and white. But no female can beat its wings so fast as to elicit the optimal response from the male. It is therefore possible to produce supra-normal models which are more effective than real females. Furthermore, this species also includes the female morph *valesina*, which is dark above in contrast to the normal females. Such females are far less attractive to the males than the normally coloured females. They could theoretically counteract this by increasing the wing-beat frequency, but this does not appear to happen. Nevertheless, the males can tell that models are not real females when they attempt to copulate, since at close range olfactory stimuli also play a part.

Similar experiments have since been carried out on butterflies which represent models or mimics in mimicry systems. It was again shown that the male at first reacts to the optical image of a presumed female. It is therefore hardly surprising that reports are encountered where a mimic male has been seen to fly after the model female and vice versa. The investigations also showed that odour plays a special role at close range, finally allowing species and sex recognition. Courtship of the wrong partner is thus rapidly broken off. For example, the males of *Hypolimnas misippus* will stop sunning themselves and approach anything that happens to fly past; they even do this with high-flying birds. They pay more attention to the pattern of the hind-wings of the partner than to the fore-wings; brown hind-wings are preferred, while white hind-wings inhibit courtship. For this reason, no female of this species can afford to imitate closely the *alsippus* form of the model *Danaus chrysippus* (a morph with white hind-wings), although this is presumably genetically possible. The most that occurs is a lightening of the hind-wings, which Stride regards as a compromise between imitation of the model and an essential consideration of the preference of the male.

In addition, there are distinct differences in the courtship between, for instance, the model *Danaus chrysippus* and its mimic *Papilio dardanus* (figure 4b). A *P. dardanus* male flies underneath a female, forcing her to land on his back. The female is then carried downwards on to a bush, and females unwilling to mate have the opportunity to fly off. A male *D. chrysippus*, on the other hand, flies above the female and dives down towards her. The male attempts to strike the female with his abdomen and then immediately flies upwards. Odours play an important role in this behaviour. The males of *Danaus* species bears two protrusible, hair-covered odour brushes at the posterior end. The male bends its abdomen sharply upwards and presses those brushes into special odour pockets on the upper side of the hind-wings. In the courtship phase, this is performed several times a day. As far as is known, chemical substances in the brush and in the pocket react together to form an odour which varies from species to species, and sometimes even from sub-species to sub-species. The males present the odour to the females when they fly over and drag the brush over the female's head.

It is thus known that the female coloration is an important feature of recognition for males of both mimetic and non-mimetic species. In some cases, particular female colour patterns are preferred. It is also known that the courtship dances of the model and the mimic differ greatly in appearance – at least in some cases – and that olfactory signals play a supporting role. But practically nothing is known of the significance of the male coloration for the female. This is predominantly due either to the fact that both sexes resemble other species and then employ olfactory orientation, or to the fact that the females look different while the males always look the same, so that experiments cannot be carried out with the females without artificially colouring the males. At the present time, the assumption that the males remain conservative in coloration to please the females is nothing more than a plausible supposition.

Burns (1966) derived a further argument for the effectiveness of mimicry from the preference shown by some organisms for particular mating partners. In North America, a black female morph of *Papilio glaucus* is found as a mimic of the inedible butterfly *Battus philenor*. This black morph is noticeably restricted to the range of distribution of the model. In places where the model is absent, as in Florida, *P. glaucus* females are black and yellow in colour, just like the males. In mating, these females are distinctly preferred to the black morphs by the similarly coloured males. But in areas where *Battus philenor* occurs, this preference is cancelled out by the selective effect exerted by predatory birds, which leave the less eligible (black) females in peace to produce offspring; the birds eat instead the females best liked by the male butterflies.

3 Mimicry and Darwinism

In 1858 and 1859, Charles Darwin and A. R. Wallace published their views on the operation of natural selection in the evolutionary change of living organisms. Catch-phrases such as 'struggle for survival' and 'survival of the fittest' began to circulate and were actively disputed, and some aspects of the theory of the evolution of living organisms met with very embittered intellectual opposition. The theory provided an explanation for special adaptations in nature which formerly required the existence of a supernatural or divine influence over life processes. It is, of course, nonsensical to assume that a gap exists in scientific thought and explanations and that this gap is proof of the existence of supernatural forces. In other words, the teleologists – those who regarded the strikingly refined adaptations of living organisms to their environmental conditions as proof of the existence of a purposive Creator – made a logical error; one can neither prove nor disprove the existence of a Creator in this way. The teleologists nevertheless felt that the new theory was a threat, and Darwin's theory of evolution was widely regarded as usurping the concept of a purposive creative force as the active agent in adaptation.

The mimicry hypothesis emerged in the middle of the Darwinian controversy and provided an ideal test-case. For this reason, the hypothesis came under numerous attacks right from the start, and these were not primarily zoological in origin. In order to understand the discussion of the mimicry problem, which has persisted up to the present day, it is necessary to consider how vigorously the concept of evolution is still dismissed in many circles. Examples of this are found even in the United States. In 1925, a teacher by the name of John Scope was taken to Court in Dayton, Tennessee because he had discussed evolution in a school subsidised with taxpayers' money. Forty years later, the situation was no different. In an extraordinarily large number of educational districts, which are very largely autonomous in the USA, instruction in the theory of evolution is prohibited. The restrictions are not legally prescribed, but the methods used are nonetheless effective. Such is the case, for example, in the state of Indiana in the immediate neighbourhood of Chicago. Only recently, the famous phylogeneticist George Gaylord Simpson called for a detailed investigation into the underlying reasons for contemporary anti-evolutionism. Yet it seems virtually impossible for anyone who goes through the world with his eyes open to overlook the changes wrought by evolution. For one thing, we possess a large range of fossil evidence showing the gradual change of organisms with time, while the case of industrial melanism described on page 51 proves that natural selection is a real force.

A study of modern biology drives home the fact that adaptation is inevitable, that is, that organisms adapt to environmental conditions. This does not mean, however, that all variation is adaptive. Further, the process of selection cannot be regarded as a metaphysical force; selection is a consequence of a quite specific causal system and selective effects are passive and automatic. This can be illustrated by an example from Wallace and Srb, which demonstrates an entirely unintentional selective process which takes place in fruit-fly cultures. The fruit-fly *Drosophila* is an important tool in genetical research, and is bred in large numbers in stoppered glass vessels. When the stopper is removed when the vessel is re-stocked with food, a large number of fruit-flies escape, since they normally attempt to fly upwards towards the light. This soon ceases because each population contains a number of abnormal individuals which have an innate inclination to head downwards rather than upwards. Naturally, these flies and their descendants remain in the vessel when it is opened. Eventually these are the sole survivors, owing to the automatic selection for those flies which voluntarily remain captive in the vessel as a result of their genetical make-up. Further examples, included in the concept of mimicry, are provided by a number of cultivated plants, and the evolution of these is discussed in the following chapter.

4 Mimetic weeds

A number of important crop plants are age-old attendants of human culture. The oldest were probably gathered because of their useful properties, the seeds then being scattered in the vicinity of human dwellings. Such seeds had a very good chance of growing into healthy plants, particularly near to waste heaps, with the result that planned sowing developed. These old cultivated crops include wheat, millet, rice, corn, flax, soya beans, rape-seed and cotton. Ecologically speaking, these are all ruderal plants, that is, those which grow on waste and garbage; all require a wide range of nutrients, which is provided by the manure. As soon as such plants are tended and cultivated by man, a certain selective pressure is introduced. The main character of all cultivated plants is the so-called giant type. The differences in size between cultivated plants and the wild form may not exactly be gigantic, but they are definitely conspicuous and they always concern those structures of use to man. The biggest are preferred, be it fruits (edible fruit, tomatoes), leaves (cabbage, lettuce), roots (carrots, sugar beet, radish), underground shoots (potatoes, Indian sunflower), above-ground shoots (kohlrabi, sugar-cane) or blossoms (fleshy inflorescences, such as cauliflower and artichokes). In many cases, other parts of the plants not required by man may increase in size; our cereals also have thicker stems and leaves, while flax plants have larger flowers and seeds.

In addition, different types may be bred within the same species. With cabbage, *Brassica oleracea* (family Cruciferae), it may be the leaves which are changed (wrinkled in kale, forming a loose head in savoy and butter-cabbage and a firm head in white and red cabbage), the shoot may be thickened (kohlrabi), or the inflorescence may be thickened and fleshy (cauliflower). The turnip is derived from the wild cabbage (*Brassica campestris* → *Brassica rapa*). One form has been selected for oil-yield (var. *silvestris*), another for thickened, turnip-like roots (late turnip; var. *rapifera*) and another for tender leaves and a tender, thickened stem (mangel-wurzel; var. *esculenta communis*). This list of well-known examples is proof of the effectiveness of selection.

In these instances, man carries out conscious selection, promoting those forms which he prefers and neglecting the others, which gradually decline in numbers. Man also selects against those useless plants which grow together with the useful plants. These are called weeds, and they are not just neglected, they are eliminated. It is therefore very interesting that some weeds have become useful plants through the process of mimicry. Man is an enemy of weeds – a predator if you like, whereas he protects and cultivates crop plants. But this difference in treatment can only be applied when it is possible to distinguish between weeds and crops. This is sometimes very difficult, since there are cases of unrelated plants which resemble one another quite closely. Furthermore, it is necessary to employ a technique which will selectively eliminate the weeds – something which is almost impossible in a field of wheat. In such a case, separation must be attempted with the harvested seeds.

The gold-of-pleasure *Camelina sativa linicola*, with its thin, unbranching stem and thin, pale leaves, resembles the flax plant *Linum usitatissimum* very closely. The flax plant belongs to the family Linaceae, the gold-of-pleasure to the Cruciferae, and both occur together in flax fields. The gold-of-pleasure is derived from the smaller, wild plant *Camelina gabrata*, which became mixed up with the flax as a weed. Since this was not noticeable, the wild plant enjoyed cultivation by man under cover of its chance camouflage. The plant of course received the same treatment as the flax. Now long stems with restricted branching are essential to tall plants growing together with others in a field, and the gold-of-pleasure gradually developed this character, which is also occasionally present where it grows in isolation. But such a similarity is not important among cultivated plants, for even conspicuous weeds cannot be removed from a flaxfield, any more than poppies or cornflowers can be removed from a cornfield. This is because the fields are too big and if one tried to pluck out the weeds by hand, too many plants would be trampled in the process. However, there is another, far more important feature. Originally, the husks of the ripe flax fruit would break cleanly and easily away from the strong frame of the partition between them. Under natural conditions, this is essential to ensure seed dispersal. But in cultivated fields, man harvests only those seeds which are still contained in the husks of the ripe flax, and at the same time, he cannot help but harvest other similarly contained seeds. Such seeds then become mixed with the flax seeds on threshing and thus enjoy human protection. In fact they have a far greater chance of dispersal than the seeds of the wild form. The husks of the gold-of-pleasure now remain closed and the limp walls of the fruit remain tender. This does not matter, however, since the sclerotic tissue formerly necessary as protection became superfluous as soon as man included the weed under his protection. Winnowing machines are used to separate the seed from the husks. The seeds of the gold-of-pleasure are different from those of the flax in both size and weight, but the important factor in winnowing is the combination of weight and size. These two features are so adjusted in the gold-of-pleasure that they are thrown exactly the same distance as the flax seeds from the winnowing machine. 'Adjusted' simply means that only those seeds which are thrown the same distance by the machine automatically end up with the flax seed. This adaptation arises through independent approximation to the selected character without any deliberate action on the part of the plant, the machine, or the human being. Back-crossing of the gold-of-pleasure with its nearest relative demonstrates that the mimetic characters of the seeds are genetically determined, being controlled by a complex of genes.

The classic example of a converted weed is rye. A particular species of grass, the wild rye *Secale montanum*, is distributed throughout the Mediterranean area, from Spain to Central Asia. One race (wild rye from Anatolia) become mixed up with wheat and barley together with corn-cockle, cornflower and wild poppy. Wheat (*Triticum*) is one of the oldest cereals in human culture. The seeds are by nature small and the panicle spindle (the end of the stalk bearing the seeds) is very fragile. Of course, man was interested in obtaining larger seeds and a more stable spindle, which would prevent damage and loss of part of the crop in transport. Under natural conditions, both of these features are completely unsuitable. First, small seeds germinate just as well as large seeds, and so the latter represents wastage of material. Secondly a rigid panicle spindle prevents natural dispersal of the seeds, and so the forms with a rigid spindle cannot survive in the wild. But when man takes over care and seed-dispersal for the plant, these selective pressures are eliminated and are instead replaced by domestic selection. The same domestic pressures practised on wheat were also exerted on the rye-weed growing in wheat fields. Hence, rye also came to develop larger seeds and more rigid spindles under the favourable, but unintentional, care of mankind. Plants with these features had a greater chance of survival and so rye was cultivated in the same direction as wheat.

There is another factor involved, however, in the development of mimicry in rye. The primitive form of wheat is an annual plant and the fields were therefore constructed for a yearly crop, but wild rye was originally a perennial and was consequently subjected to regular extermination, together with other perennial weeds, when the earth was tilled after harvest. Now rye does occasionally throw off annual forms in the wild. If such an aberrant form were to produce seed in the first year while growing as a weed in wheat fields, then the seeds would be harvested with those of wheat, and come under the same selective pressures as for wheat. In this way, the annual, hard-spindled rye-weed evolved from the perennial, weak-spindled wild rye without attracting the attention of man. The wild form of the weed can still be found in Turkistan and Persia. Long ago, this weed accompanied wheat to the West and more or less thrust itself upon human culture, since it is less demanding and tougher than its model, the wheat plant. The less favourable the climate and the soil are for wheat, the more likely it is that rye alone will remain. This proved to be true not only during the spread in distribution of the two plants to the North, but also during the spread of wheat cultures in mountainous areas in the original area of distribution. Since rye had already surreptitiously acquired the characters of cultivated plants, man deliberately continued to cultivate the plant until it became a separate crop.

The same was true of oats (*Avena*) which grow upon the scantiest soil and represent an important source of food. This plant was also a wild grass species (wild oats *Avena fatua*) and began to grow as a weed in wheat and barley fields. The weed was not conspicuous and was in any case impossible to remove. As a result, this plant gradually spread to the North-west with the cultivated cereals until it reached central Europe. Oat plants with rigid spindles were harvested without losing their seed, together with the cereals, and then the seeds were sown in the following year. The wild oat plant slowly developed into a ubiquitous weed and eventually came to be the sole survivor in poor climates where the true cereal plants perished. Since the seed was of some use, it was harvested in times of want and finally came to be cultivated as an independent oat crop. The spindles of the wild oats are fragile, as is required for natural dispersal. The plant also has coarse ears, which serve as protection during the dormant winter phase on the ground. The ears bear long, stiff hairs, which helps the dispersal of the seeds by wind, while a tough beard aids in boring into the ground. But under human cultivation, those with tough spindles had the advantage in dispersal and seeds which were liberated only by heavy threshing were favoured. The hairs, the beard and the coarse ears became superfluous, since man had taken over protection and dispersal, and they have almost disappeared from cultivated oats.

There is one plant parasite, the dodder (Convolvulaceae), which has come under human cultivation. The flax-dodder *Cuscuta epilinum* grows as a creeper around flax and linseed plants and damages them. The typical small seeds of the parasite can be separated from the larger flax seeds, but larger seeds from the flax parasite automatically became mixed with the harvested seed. Today, man cultivates and spreads a special mutant of the flax-dodder, unintentionally and contrary to his own interests. The necessary seed size is achieved by the production of double instead of the normal single seeds. In this case, a genuine parasite is imitating the most important character of a plant under man's protection and thus remains largely unmolested. By studying cultivated plants, it is possible to assess the advantages and disadvantages of different characteristics in model and mimic, since man himself decides what is advantageous and carries out conscious selection, which is something that is not true of many other mimicry systems.

5 Definitions and objections

Bates restricted his definition of mimicry to 'resemblance in external appearance, shapes and colours between members of widely distinct families'. A more common definition, particularly in school text-books, is 'the imitation of a protected animal species by an unprotected species'. At the International Zoological Congress in Washington, 1963, the following definition was provided: 'mimicry is the close resemblance of one organism to another which, because it is unpalatable and conspicuous, is recognised and avoided by some predators at some times'. This latter has a more sophisticated air, but it was only intended as a heading for the cases to be dealt with and not really as a restricted definition. One could be almost malicious and state that these definitions themselves are examples of mimicry, presumptions disguised in the uniform of principles. These presumptions are admittedly obvious ones to make, and supposed examples of mimicry supporting them soon flowed in. Even today, new examples are always turning up.

The concept of mimicry was almost suffocated in the cradle. The greatest threat originated from the mentally idle who regarded the catchword mimicry as a substitute for an explanation. Also, some attempts were made from the very beginning to construct supplementary clauses to narrow the definition. The best known of these, quoted to the present day, are those given by Wallace and listed in Poulton's *The colours of animals, their meaning and use* (London, 1890). These clauses are given below, together with a critical examination of each concept.

1. 'that the imitative species occur in the same area and occupy the same station as the imitated'. This increases the probability that a predator will affect both parties concerned. Nevertheless, the model could live in Africa and the mimic in Europe, or vice versa, if the deceived predator were a migratory bird.

2. 'that the imitators are always the more defenceless'. It will be seen later on in the discussion of Mertensian mimicry among coral snakes that the more offensive party may occasionally be the mimic.

3. 'that the imitators are always less numerous in individuals'. What

is meant here is that the deceived animal should encounter the mimic less often than the model. This is true when the deceived animal must learn to recognise model and mimic and when positive and negative experiences carry equal weight. But it is known from various learning experiments that when an animal has to learn about warning coloration, negative experiences or punishment stimuli (such as inedibility) can have a stronger and more lasting effect than positive experiences. Accordingly, it should be expected that there would be an excess of mimics over models in proportion to the degree of predominance of negative experiences over positive ones. We shall see on page 164 that the mimic must be less common in cases where the negative experiences are provided by the mimic itself, as in aggressive mimicry. But when the deceived animal possesses an innate reaction to the model (examples of this will be given later), the number of mimics can be virtually unlimited.
4. 'that the imitators differ from the bulk of their allies'. When this condition applies, our attention is of course most easily attracted. The most remarkable cases of mimicry are those where close relatives form divergent series (figures 1 and 2), each series corresponding to different models. It is nevertheless highly possible that groups of closely related species may be similar mimics of the same model. Of course, it must always be remembered that species can look very different from their relatives because of adaptations which have nothing to do with mimicry.
5. 'that the imitation, however minute, is external and visible only, never extending to internal characters or to such as do not affect the external appearance'. This criterion, like the previous one is aimed at defining mimicry as a special adaptation. But if one of two closely related species, both of which are poisonous and possess similar warning coloration, should secondarily lose its poisonous qualities, it would become a mimic and yet resemble its model in almost all its non-mimetic characters. Apart from this, Poulton only speaks of optical characters. In cases where olfactory signals play a part, the production of odours may require the development of internal similarities which themselves have no signalling function.

These five requirements, if fulfilled, indeed increase the probability that any given case of mimicry will be correctly diagnosed. But such supplementary clauses cannot be used as a definition of mimicry in general, though this is unfortunately often attempted. We shall return to this question of definitions at the end of the book after we have examined a large number of examples.

Strangely enough, the objections presented here are seldom, if ever, raised by opponents of the mimicry theory. These opponents have other arguments, the most cherished of which asserts that warning and cryptic (camouflage) patterns cannot provide any conspicuous advantage, since there are far greater numbers of species which survive without such protection. In America, this objection is succinctly described as the refrigerator fallacy. Refrigeration cannot be so advantageous as is commonly assumed, since so many people get by without one. It is naturally possible to provide good reasons for the fact that many people who would very much like to have a refrigerator have to make do without. But how are we to determine whether the poisonous adder or the spiny hedgehog would not prefer to have a black-and-yellow warning pattern if only they could develop one? It is very difficult to explain why something has *not* been developed, but this does not amount to proof against the usefulness of this something to animals which already possess it. No one would seriously maintain that the human brain does not have advantages simply because all other animals manage with an inferior brain.

Another argument takes roughly the following form: camouflage of soldiers, weapons or buildings in war is ineffective, since camouflaged objects are also located and destroyed. This is of course absurd. It is equally absurd to object to the theory of warning coloration on the grounds that the bee-eater *Merops* has chosen to specialise on the allegedly protected bees. There is no such thing as complete protection, but even partial protection is thankfully acknowledged, as it is by insurance companies and aeroplane passengers. There are always some organisms which eat those generally regarded as poisonous or unpalatable. Rabbits eat the extremely

Figure 5. The North American darkling-beetle *Eleodes* stands on its head when disturbed and sprays a defensive secretion at the attacker from glands in the abdomen. A very similar beetle, *Megasida*, assumes the same posture but contains no defensive secretion.

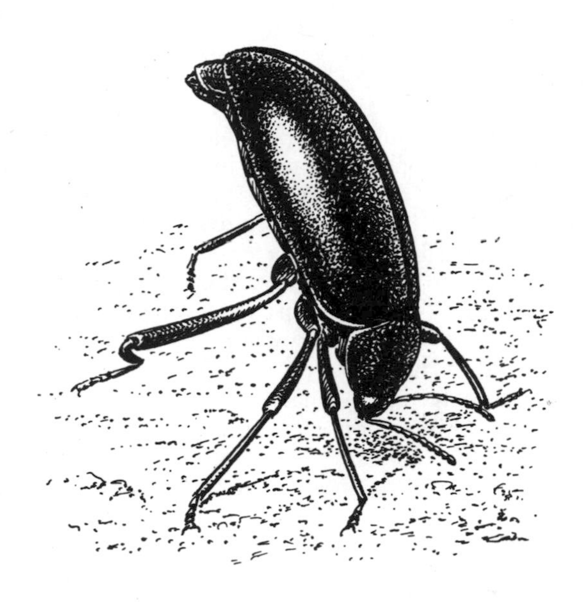

poisonous toadstool *Amanita phalloides* and the hyrax *Procavia abessina* eats the highly poisonous plant *Phytolacca dodecandra*, which also does not harm the domestic hen. The red-backed shrike *Lanius collurio* can skilfully remove the stings of bees and wasps. In Florida, the caterpillar of the feather-moth *Trichoptilus parvulus*, scarcely one half centimetre in length, eats the stalked glands of the sundew *Drosera*. Eisner and Shepherd found that this caterpillar starts its meal with the sticky secreted droplet which the plant employs to trap other insects. The mongoose eats snakes – there is no limit to the number of examples which could be quoted.

Unpalatable, defensive, protected – these terms are only valid within limits. There is no all-or-none effect; the small additional advantages which accrue are only evident in particular situations. This means that the relevant circumstances in each case should be examined, something which the all-or-none fanatics tend not to do.

On close analysis, all opponents of the theory of protective coloration are in an unfortunate situation. To disprove the existence of protective patterns is just as impossible as to disprove the influence of constellations upon the fate of human beings, as postulated by astrologers. But it is possible to show that such a hypothesis is very improbable, at least in given individual cases, by demonstrating that it is superfluous for the explanation of the phenomena which it is supposed to clarify. It is of course, possible to patch together a number of explanations for every observed phenomenon. A proof for protective patterns must include:

1. The demonstration that a predator or other signal-receiver responds to the signals involved in the manner postulated.
2. The demonstration that this response is an advantage to the organism that transmits the signals.

Camouflage has also been touched upon in this discussion, since it represents an additional form of protective patterning, different from both warning patterns and, in the case of mimicry, from false warning patterns. The proof that a signal-receiver responds must be provided in all cases. Camouflage is directed at the substrate. Animals living on snow or ice in polar regions (polar bears, snow foxes, snow hares, ptarmigans, snowly owls and gyr falcons) are all white in appearance. Looper caterpillar look like small twigs, while the aplacophoran mollusc *Neomenia corrallophila* is red-and-white in colour like the arms of the red coral between which it sits. Cryptic coloration, or camouflage, will be discussed briefly in the next chapter so that it can be compared with mimicry later on.

6 Camouflage

Industrial melanism

Melanin is a black pigment common in the animal kingdom, and causes a black coloration called melanism. Industrial melanism refers to a predominance of this black pigment in animals in industrial areas, an effect which is due not to dirt but to hereditary transmission of black colour. The colour of members of the same animal species often varies, so that light and quite dark specimens can be found, as in the case of the North American white-footed mouse *Peromyscus*. As might be expected, each colour type can be at an advantage in that it enjoys better cryptic protection against predators on the right background. Light and dark mice of this species were placed in chambers with light and dark backgrounds and exposed to hunting owls of various species. The owls caught mainly dark individuals on a light background and light individuals on a dark background. Cryptic coloration also applies to many insects, which are almost impossible to discern on particular substrates. There are many moths which rest on light substrates during the day, for example on light bark that is covered with lichens. The moths sit with spread wings and the colour and patterning of the wings often resembles that of the substrate so exactly that it is virtually impossible to find them.

In the past few decades, the peppered moth *Biston betularia* has risen to fame. This moth is, or was, normally white with a covering of black spots and stripes. Melanic forms always occurred here and there, but as rarities known as the *carbonaria* form. The difference between this form and the normal *betularia* is based on a specific dominant gene. Dark peppered moths sit on the same resting sites as the normal forms and are thus very conspicuous. This was the case in 1850, at least. But dark animals were no longer rarities by 1895; on the contrary, 95 per cent of these moths in the neighbourhood of Manchester were dark forms. Since the peppered moth has one generation of offspring per year, it could be calculated that the dark form must have had a 30 per cent better chance of survival than the normal moth in order to become so well established in the course of fifty years. It was fairly obvious that the cause must lie with predators. In actual fact, rising industrialisation at the end of the last century spread soot around industrial centres and blackened everything to some degree. Most important, the light birch trunks became darkened in these areas.

When the light and dark moths settled together on the darkened trunks, the light ones were conspicuous and were eaten, or so the simplest explanation ran. Other explanations were put forward, however. Hasebroek assumed that the pollution of the air altered the organism physiologically so that inordinate amounts of black pigment were produced, while Harrison believed that the lead in the soot covering the leaves increased the rate of mutation so that far more genetically-determined black forms arose. Eventually the still unsolved problem was taken up by Dr Kettlewell in 1953 and tackled experimentally. Kettlewell obtained a total of 3,000 peppered moth pupae, including both light and dark forms. The moths were marked on the underside with coloured spots as soon as they hatched, which ensured later distinction from wild forms without affecting prospective predators. These moths were freed on tree-trunks at a rate of about fifty a day. Both light and dark forms were liberated and if all of one form disappeared further individuals were added. The fate of the moths was observed from a hide until they disappeared from view. It soon became obvious that insect-hunting birds indeed carried off the moths, the main predators being spotted flycatchers *Muscicapa striata*, nuthatches *Sitta europaea*, yellow-hammers *Emberiza citrinella*, robins *Erithacus rubecula*, redstarts *Phoenicurus phoenicurus*, hedge sparrows *Prunella modularis* and song-thrushes *Turdus ericetorum*. In a rural area with many light, lichen-covered trunks, where no free-living dark forms were to be found, 190 of the freed moths were taken by the birds in a short space of time; 164 were dark and 26 light, thus showing that the dark animals were presumably as conspicuous for optically hunting birds as for us.

But of course many of the liberated moths were not seen to be eaten. In order to gain some indication of the numbers surviving,

Kettlewell set up mercury lamps at night, together with a series of small cages containing females. Since the light, with its strong ultraviolet component, attracts males more easily than females, only males were released. With these two methods, the captured males included 4·7 percent of the released dark forms and 13·7 per cent of the light forms.

Both these experiments were similarly performed in an industrial area, where the trees were dirty and devoid of lichens, and dark forms represented 85 per cent of the free-living moths. Observation showed that the birds took more light than dark moths of those released and recaptures included roughly twice as many dark as light forms. These experiments were repeated two years later with the same result.

The predominance of one form in the recapture could be attributed to different causes, such as to a different reaction to light of the females, or to different viability, or to differences in range. These possibilities are improbable for various reasons, and the diametrically opposed results from the two areas (sooty and soot-free) exclude these explanations. The remaining possibility is that the two forms suffer predation to different extents, as was observed. Further investigations revealed other differences between the two forms of the peppered moth. The caterpillar of the light form eats more rapidly and pupates earlier than that of the dark form. The light forms probably exploit the still uncontaminated young foliage, while the dark forms spend much time in excreting the poisonous substances taken up with the food. In addition, the viability of the black form *carbonaria* has increased between the beginning of this century and the present time; the white form was at first more viable, but the reverse is now the case. Further, *carbonaria* was not so intensively pigmented a hundreds years ago as it is today, indicating that the dominance of the *carbonaria* gene has increased.

Industrial melanism among moths is one of the most impressive examples of the operation of certain selective factors on the evolution of animals, in this case affecting protective coloration. I have only mentioned the peppered moth, but of 780 English moth species, 70 are already on the way to industrial melanism while some even have melanic caterpillars. In some cases, the inheritance and selective function of melanism have been investigated in detail, as in the peppered moth. The results are similar, but the viability of homo- and heterozygotes and the dominance of the melanic gene vary. Industrial melanism also occurs elsewhere, as in the industrial areas of North America, where sometimes as much as 90 per cent of a moth population may be melanic. The relevant data were summarised by Owen in 1961.

Cryptic behaviour

Any cryptic coloration must blend with the background of the animal. Thus, an animal which alternates between different sites of activity or rest must adjust its camouflage at each move. This can be done in two ways: either the animal alters its coloration to fit the background or it searches for a background which matches the coloration.

The first method presupposes that the animal is able to alter its coloration, and this, in fact, is widespread among animals. Colour change may also reflect the mood of the animal, and then occurs regardless of the background. Colour-change is achieved in a variety of ways. The crab-spider *Misumena vatia* transfers a liquid pigmented material from the intestine to the skin to turn yellow and withdraws the fluid to change back to white. This spider sits on yellow or white flowers and traps insects without using a web, preying particularly on bees. Only female spiders are able to adapt their colour to the background and even they can only do so to a limited extent. Many flatfish, such as plaice and sole, are extremely adaptable in their coloration (figure 6). The skin contains several groups of variously coloured cells whose contents can be spread over a large area or be reduced to a minimum area. The pigment cells, which occur over the entire body, are arranged in groups, and each group can function separately. An amazing number of colours and

Figure 6. Many flatfish provide excellent examples of adaptation of the body coloration to that of the environment. It takes only a few hours for these fish to adjust their coloration to correspond with the substrate. Although the eyes are necessary for this change, the fish need not see its own body, for the correct colour pattern is achieved even when the body is covered with sand. The sole (*Solea solea*) shown here, about 11 cm long, can scarcely be made out on sand (bottom), but is conspicuous on a dark artificial background (top).

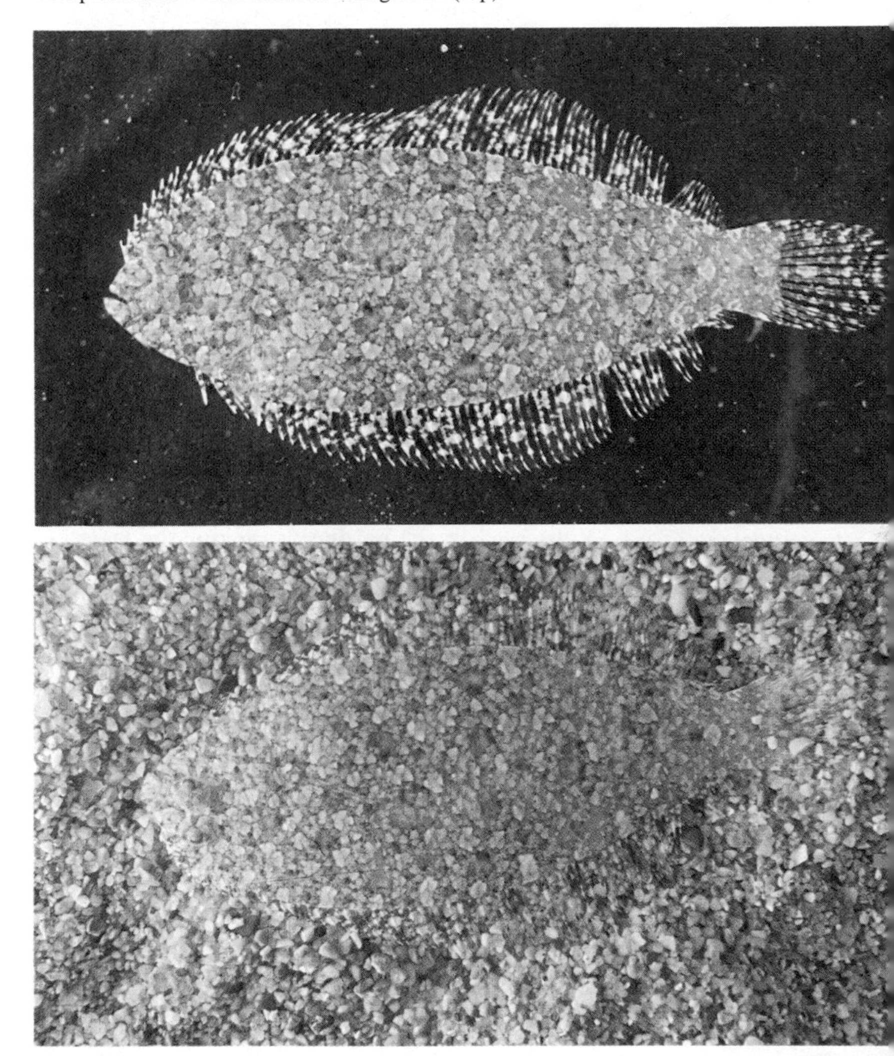

colour patterns is produced by bringing into action different combinations of groups containing different pigments. The change in pattern to agree with a particular background is ensured by complex nervous coordination in which the eye is particularly important. But the fish does not compare its own colour with that of the substrate and then carry out adjustments until agreement is reached. Instead, it sees the substrate and then selects a particular colour-switch. This can easily be demonstrated if one eliminates the animal's ability to obtain feed-back information on the success of the colour-change. If the body of a flatfish is covered with sand so that only its eyes remain unsubmerged, the coloration of the fish still correctly adapts to fit the substrate, although the body is invisible.

Some animals obtain their cryptic coloration from the environment. The spider-crabs *Hyas* and *Maja* collect pieces of algae and then fix them on their backs, either by sticking the pieces with an oral secretion or by impaling them on tiny spines. The larva of the lily beetle *Crioceris lilii*, a member of the leaf-beetle family (*Chrysomelidae*), can be observed in the garden to devour the leaves of lilies with gusto. These larvae are at first difficult to spot, although they are brick-red, because they sit under a self-made pile of green faecal pellets stacked on the body. All that one sees on the plants are piles of faeces, which appear to move around and eat continuously. It is easy to see how these larvae assemble their camouflage to protect them from ants and other insect enemies, if the existing layer of faecal matter is removed.

In the cases mentioned, the adaptation of colour to fit the background has an obvious air of activity, but adaptive colour changes can also be achieved by more passive means. Over-wintering pupae of the swallowtail butterfly *Papilio machaon* look green when attached to plant stems and grey when attached to tree-trunks or stones. The coloration is determined by the site of pupation and the prevailing light-exposure during a sensitive phase shortly preceding pupation.

These animals, then, adapt to fit their particular backgrounds, but it occasionally happens that an animal alters its surroundings

Figure 7. The Asiatic spider *Cyclosa mulmeinensis* fools spider-hunting predators by building a number of pseudo-platforms which appear to be occupied by spiders. In the illustration, the real spider is sitting in the normal platform in the middle of the almost invisible web. The probability of a predator capturing the real spider is thus only 1 in 3 in this case.

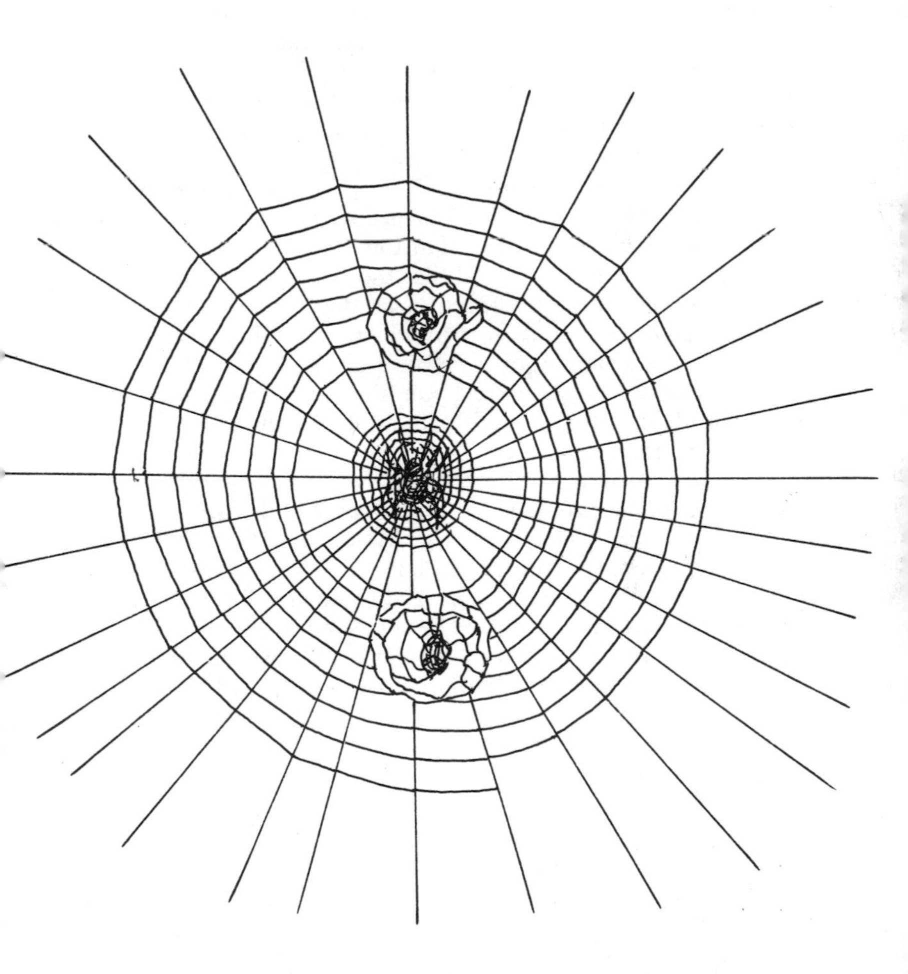

to fit its own appearance. A number of South American caterpillars cut pieces out of leaves to correspond to their own size and suspend them from threads alongside. The Malayan spider *Cyclosa insulana* bears silvery hairs and builds a glittering web as a juvenile, whereas the adults are brown and powder their nests with brown wood dust. The caterpillar of the atlas moth *Attacus edwardsii* in Assam spins itself a case on pupation, as do all caterpillars of the family Saturniidae. This species pupates between the two halves of a folded leaf. The leaf-pedicle is bitten through after it has been attached to a twig so that the pupa eventually hangs in a withered leaf. Kuyten observed that the caterpillar previously does this to a number of adjacent leaves so that they wither alongside. The withered leaves stand out from the surrounding green leaves so that a predator which inquisitively examines them will find nothing in the majority and lose interest. On the other hand, if the predator should by chance find the leaf containing the pupa, it will eagerly examine the adjacent leaves. It will then be disappointed and the chances are that it will refrain from investigating withered leaves again. The same principle is employed by the spider *Cyclosa mulmeinensis*, which is common in Malaya and Siam. This spider sits on the hub of its web with retracted legs. The hub is surrounded by a broad reinforcement zone ringed by an area free of spiral silk; the spider is thus easy to find. The spider binds remains of its prey together in bundles of the same size as itself, suspends them somewhere on the web and surrounds them with special threads. This makes it considerably more difficult to decide where the spider is actually sitting, since each heap is set in the middle of a hub (figure 7). Hingston has described many similar spider tricks, all designed to lead predators astray.

Where an animal is not capable of colour change it must seek out a suitable background before resting. This is actually the most common type of camouflage. Leaf-green animals sit on leaves, bark-coloured animals sit on tree-trunks and sand-coloured animals sit on sand. This adaptation becomes particularly obvious when the animal alters its colour and habitat at the same time, as with age. The caterpillar of the Noctuid moth *Hyloicus pinastri* is blue-green in colour in the juvenile stage, is one to three centimetres in length, bears six longitudinal white stripes, and rests on pine needles during the day. It is very difficult to pick out because of its colour pattern. But after the last moult the caterpillar has a completely different appearance: it is about five centimetres long and brown in colour and bears irregular white and black flecks. In this phase, the caterpillar rests on the brown twigs bearing the needles. Exactly the same thing happens with another caterpillar, *Ellopia prosapiaria*. In the last phase, this species even carries gnarled projections and folds on its skin in addition to the bark coloration. The Geometrid pine moth *Bupalus piniarius* caterpillar, on the other hand, always looks green with white longitudinal stripes 'because' it always sits on pine needles. In these cases, Herrebout and his colleagues proved that the cryptic coloration of the caterpillars makes them more difficult to find, not only for us but also for bird predators.

Cryptic polymorphism

Clarke and Sheppard, who explained the hereditary make-up of the mimetic characters of the African butterfly *Papilio dardanus*, discovered an interesting use of camouflage with caterpillars of a related species occurring in the same region – *Papilio demodocus*. The caterpillars of this species feed largely on citrus plants and related rues in certain areas of South Africa. But some feed on umbelliferous plants, a completely separate group. The two types of caterpillar look very different and the effect has been shown to be independent of the food-plant – it is genetically determined. If the caterpillars sit on the wrong plant, particularly when a umbilliferous caterpillar is placed on a citrus plant, they rapidly fall prey to birds. There is thus a distinct dimorphism in the adaptation of the two caterpillars, each being adapted towards a particular food-plant, but it is not clear how the caterpillars find the right plant. There may be a dimorphism in behaviour.

The moth *Erynnyis ello* occurs in the Galapagos. Curio found that the caterpillars existed in three different colours, which he called grey, brown and green for simplicity. All forms have the same diet, the leaves of the Mancanillo tree, but differ in their behaviour. The green caterpillar rests on the leaves, whereas the other two types rest on twigs; each is very well camouflaged where it sits. They are heavily preyed upon by finches, mocking-birds, and wood warblers, and so this complicated type of camouflage is presumably worthwhile. But why do the caterpillars look different? One would think that a single good cryptic pattern with the appropriate behaviour would suffice. On observing the behaviour of the insectivorous birds, however, it can easily be shown that several cryptic patterns are better than one. Sooner or later a bird finds a caterpillar, perhaps because it treads upon it or because the caterpillar is badly situated. The bird then begins to search systematically for objects of similar appearance and soon finds further caterpillars of the same type, as was shown both in a series of observations and with experiments. This occurs whether or not the caterpillars are well camouflaged where they are sitting. Since the bird is preoccupied with looking for a particular pattern, it completely overlooks caterpillars with other cryptic patterns. The same explanation is provided by Owen, who discovered in 1961 that two different organisms, the snail *Limicolaria martensiana* and the beetle *Philaemus spumarius*, exhibit very pronounced polymorphism, and both occur at unusually high densities in African areas.

Mimetic groups

Most examples of mimicry concern single individuals which resemble a model in colour, behaviour, or both. There are examples, however, where groups of animals and not individuals resemble a *single* model.

The best known example is provided by the flattid bugs (cicadas within the Fulgorid group). In East Africa it is possible to find a particular plant with extremely beautiful inflorescences (figure 9).

The individual flowers are about half a centimetre in height, look rather like broom flowers, and are arranged around a vertical stem like the flowers of the lupine. Experienced botanists have taken this plant for *Tinnaea* or *Sesamopteris* and found themselves suddenly holding a bare stem after plucking the 'flower'. The flower had not fallen off – it had flown away! The 'flower' consists of cicadas, either *Ityraea gregorii* or *Oyarina nigritarsus*. Even individual squatting animals are so similar to separate flowers that observers are repeatedly misled. Hinde saw these insects individually and in groups on horizontal twigs or between leaves near Kitui (figure 8), while China and several other workers have seen them as 'inflorescences' on vertical stems. Professor Leakey, the discoverer of *Zinjanthropus* in the Olduvai Gorge in East Africa, is well aquainted with these vertically squatting insects, since he was present at the Coryndon Museum in Nairobi at a time when several generations of the insects were bred in captivity. It is possible that the number of species involved in this group mimicry is even greater than supposed.

Ityraea nigrocincta possesses a further peculiarity in that both sexes have two morphs, a green form and a yellow form. These two morphs may squat together, and the green forms tend to sit at the top of the stem, especially on vertical stems, with the yellow forms below. The result in an extremely convincing 'inflorescence', because the true flowers of inflorescences often open progressively from base to apex, so that green buds are still present at the tip when the base is covered with open flowers. A similar dimorphism in behaviour and coloration aiding in camouflage is also known in other insects, but these are never found in such large groups.

Coloured plates of cicada-inflorescences often include a mistake, however: the artist enthusiastically portrays the upper (green) animals as being smaller that the lower (yellow-red) forms, whereas they are actually equal in size. It is doubtful whether nature invents such things merely for the sake of leading a few botanists astray, but there are unfortunately no records of other organisms being misled by these insects. This, however, is due to the fact that

Figure 8 (*left*). The insectivorous mantid *Hymenopus coronatus* (top) lives on the red flowers of an orchid in Malaysia. It resembles these flowers so closely that insects even search for nectar on the mantid, for which they pay with their lives. Bottom right: the snail-like caterpillar of the Purple Emperor *Apatura iris*. Bottom left: the African cicida *Ityraea nigrocincta*. The cicada occurs as green and yellow morphs which sit on twigs and mimic flowers.

Figure 9 (*right*). The related species *Ityraea gregorii* even group themselves to look like inflorescences.

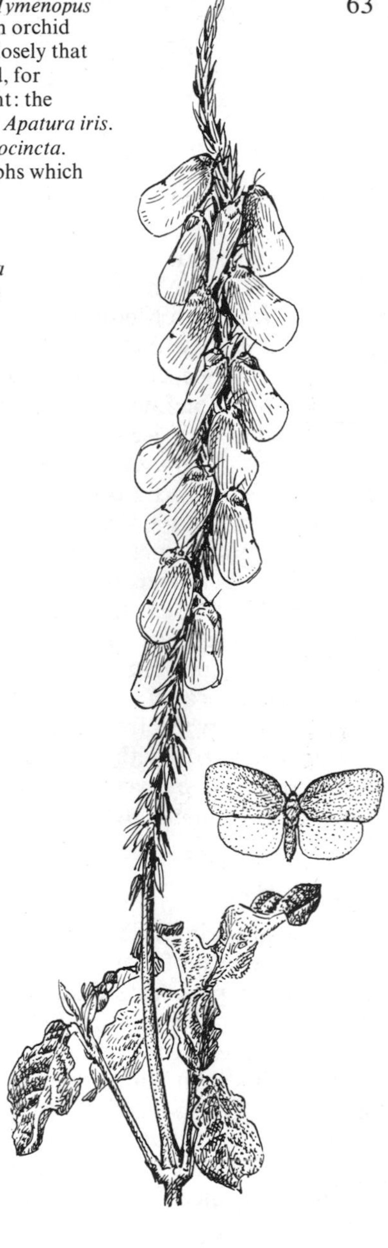

nobody has yet conducted a serious investigation.

In another case, the misled organism has in fact been identified, but we still do not know the name of the mimetic animal. This was pointed out to me by Professor Koenig of Vienna. He once collected sand from the Mediterranean coast in the vicinity of Portofino in Northern Italy for the aquaria at his biological station. Later, he discovered a beautiful marine anemone sitting in the sand in one aquarium and had no idea where it came from. The next day, there was a further surprise – there were two anemones, each half the size of the first. On the following day, there was again one large anemone. This was a downright impossibility, so Koenig transferred the animal to a smaller aquarium in order to observe it more closely. It then emerged that it was not an anemone at all, but consisted of numerous worms, each resembling the common *Tubifex*, which crept through the sand in a chain like that formed by some caterpillars. This could easily be seen through the glass wall of the aquarium. The worms eventually emerged somewhere in the sand, formed a bundle of obliquely radiating 'tentacles' and even curled up the free tips of these 'tentacles'. Small fish, which usually eat worms with relish, swam round the bundle in an obvious arc, thinking they were sea-anemones equipped with a protective array of stinging tentacles.

Eye-spots

Because of their tendency to fix the attention of human beings, the so-called eye-spots found on various animals such as butterflies, caterpillars, peacock's feathers and so on are a very well known phenomenon. There are all stages from simple round black spots, which scarcely contrast with their background, through black spots with a light contrast ring, and on to startingly impressive eye markings. Eye-spots of some types constitute a major group among animal patterns, but we do not know very much about the part they play. The name eye-spot simply indicates that *we* are reminded of an eye. But since this pattern was not developed for our benefit, we

Figure 10. The sudden display of eye-spots in times of danger frightens off insectivorous birds. For this reason, eye-spots are very common in insects. Left: the caterpillar of the Malayan butterfly *Ophideres fullonica.* Right: the South American peacock butterfly *Automeris memusae*, which covers or exposes its eye-spots by movements of the fore-wings.

need objective evidence of the actual receivers of these signals and of their relationships to the eye-spot carriers. Examining the immense range of eye-spots in nature it does not take long before the large number of possible signal-receivers and eye-spot carriers, and relationships between them, becomes insurmountable.

The first important point is that not every round, black spot necessarily represents an incomplete eye-spot. Droplets are also round, and the Russian Porschinsky in 1893 even expressed the opinion that all eye-like spots on insects were dummies of glands with an extruded poison droplet. On the other hand, some ichthyologists believe that the many small, round, light spots on the flanks of some coral fish are intended to resemble bubbles, which would theoretically help to camouflage the animals in the clouds of bubbles produced by breakers on the reef. These round spots will not be discussed here, however. Suffice it to say that not every round spot enclosed in a ring of contrasting colour represents an eye-spot. The egg-spots found on some fish have nothing to do with eye-mimicry, as will be explained later. These spots and a number of others are the reverse of eye-spots in that a light spot is surrounded by a dark ring. Such 'negative' eye-spots can also be found in butterflies whose closest relatives exhibit normal eye-spots, and one is led to assume that both have the same basic function. Then we have the very conspicuous markings on the back of the ears of big cats (particularly clear in the serval); the remarkable markings on the posterior of the head of the American sparrow-hawk *Falco sparverius*, and the less conspicuous but similar 'occipital face' of the pigmy owl *Glaucidium* have all been called eye-spots. In all these cases, nothing is known about the function of the signal.

It is often claimed that eye-spots resemble actual eyes by chance. It is argued that these signals simply attract particular attention, round spots with a contrasting border being unusual and surprise-inducing patterns. It is difficult to get round this argument. The only counter-evidence as yet comes from the fact that eye-spots often bear an asymmetrical highlight in the 'pupil'. An investigation to determine which patterns are particularly conspicuous for human beings showed that the best results were achieved with round spots containing a central contrast point and surrounded by a contrasting ring – a design that has been used in the rear lights of some American status cars. However, the investigations rarely included comparative tests with eccentric contrast spots or rings. Moreover, the tests showed that equilateral triangular spots are just as conspicuous. Yet spots of this type are scarcely ever found in animals. Under water neither droplets nor highlights exist, and no highlight-spots are known to occur on water-animal's 'eye-spots'.

The highlight is an unsuitable factor in distinguishing eye mimicry from droplet mimicry. Other supporting evidence must be used, and then it appears likely that eyes are the models. But if this is correct, the models can apply only to vertebrate eyes. The complex

Figure 11. Blest carried out experiments in which eye-spot models (below) were projected alongside mealworms just as birds were about to peck at the mealworms. He thus roughly copied the sudden exposure of eye-spots by butterflies and was able to determine the optimum repellent pattern.

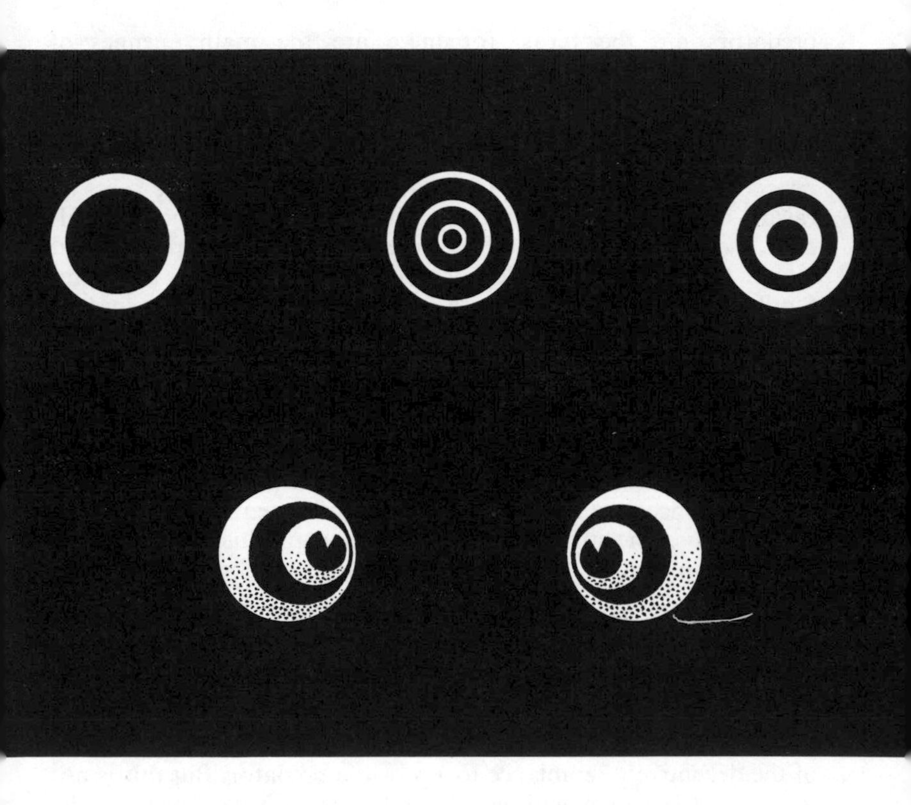

eyes of insects and crustaceans are hardly conspicuous and differ in appearance to the vertebrate eye. Only the eyes of the cephalopods (cuttlefish, etc.) correspond in detail to the vertebrate eye. Since the cephalopods are marine predators, their eyes, as also those of fish, could function as shock signals exactly as the eyes of many terrestrial vertebrates.

If this plausible, but inconclusive, argument is accepted, the main candidates as possible models and probably as signal-receiving predators are the birds, for these are the main enemies of insects. Blest (1957) tackled this problem experimentally. He tested various butterflies equipped with eye-spots on yellow-hammers which he had reared in captivity. These inexperienced birds regularly drew back when a threatened butterfly (for example, the peacock-butterfly *Nymphalis io*) suddenly displayed its eye-spots by raising its hind-wings and retracting the fore-wings. When the coloured scales of such butterflies were removed, the birds did not retreat from the resulting 'eye-less' butterflies, and they ate them. Similar results are obtained with other birds and with other insects. Blest also carried out experiments with dummies; he presented yellow hammers, chaffinches and great-tits with mealworms on a plate and suddenly projected patterns of various kinds to the left and right of the food when the tested bird arrived to eat (figure 11). All the birds, which normally ate mealworms readily, drew back more noticeably when presented with circular patterns (single and multiple concentric rings) than when confronted with crosses or parallel bars. The strongest shock effect was produced by a pair of eccentric rings closely resembling converging vertebrate eyes. In the wild, where the bird roams around searching for food, the retreat response to a signal of this kind is even more marked; and the bird seeks food elsewhere. It is already known from other investigations of bird behaviour that the eyes of a predator are important sign stimuli in recognition and flight by birds. On this basis, it can be postulated that the eye-spots of insects scare birds away because of the deceptive resemblance to a possible predator. But this is not to say that this explanation holds as a general rule. For example, social corvids have an inhibition preventing them from pecking companions in the eye. Of course, it is not known whether this stems from a fear of the eyes of predators; it is equally uncertain whether predatory bird eyes provided the original model. It could be that predator eyes are avoided because the fleeing bird avoids such patterns as a matter of course for some unknown reason.

In the dummy experiments described above, it was found that large eyes scared more than small eyes. Very small, round spots,

Figure 12. Particularly striking eye-spots are found on various fish, as on the east Asian fresh-water feather-back *Notopterus chitala* (top left), and on the dorsal surface of the flatfish *Monochirus quadriocellatus* (bottom left). Eye-spots also occur on the shell of the Burmese soft-shelled turtle *Trionyx hurum* (right)

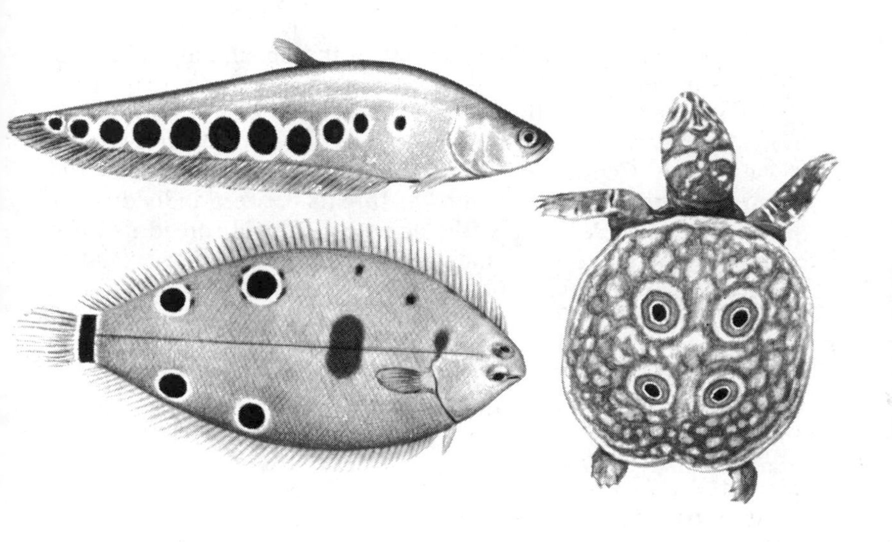

also resembling eyes, can actually stimulate pecking. Spots of this type occur along the edge of the wings of many butterflies, and experiments indicate that these spots steer the pecks of a bird away from the butterflies' bodies and on to the less vulnerable wing zone. I have found a similar effect with the eye-spots of various coral fish. The small fish *Runula* (discussed in more detail on page 165) directs its bites on larger fish mainly towards the eyes or their vicinity. The fish bites off pieces of skin, attacks very rapidly and is often mis-directed by conspicuous eye-spots at the posterior end of its victim; the real eye of the victim is often submerged in a dark mask. Many other vertebrates do this as well; so this may probably be taken as a further argument showing that the eyes at least have an important signal function. Herring-gull chicks, which peck at the red beak of the parents when begging for food, preferred a rosette-like ringed red-white spot in a dummy experiment, as long as the spot contained a similar amount of red. In this case, concentric rings increase the efficiency of the signal, but the scaring effect is completely lacking.

The significance of the many conspicuous and beautiful eye-spots in many fish (figure 12) is unknown. The opercular eye-spots of the sunfish (Centrarchidae) and various cichlid fish provide one example where the spots are used as threats between individuals of the same species. A fish directly facing a rival will spread its operculum so that the 'eyes', which are located just as they would be expected on an actual head of the same size, give the impression of an extra large head seen from the front. In some cichlids, the ring around the eye-spot has the same colour as the iris, but this is not true in all cases. It remains to be seen whether some fish go so far as to mimic the eye of a definite species and not just an eye in general.

Two heads better than one

Many animals exhibit eye-spots at the hind end of the body. This has given rise to the belief that eye-spots are there to mislead predators, which normally orient towards the head and thus snap into empty space when the prey suddenly darts to the wrong side. But in no single case has anyone been able to demonstrate that an animal with eyespots, even the oft-quoted West Indian butterfly fish *Chaetodon capistratus*, enjoys such protection. The butterfly fish has a particularly conspicuous eye-spot at the rear end of each flank. It has even been maintained that this fish swims backwards in the sea and then slips away in the other direction as a last-minute reaction to a predatory fish aiming at the false head. This may be true, but I have never been able to observe such behaviour and have never found a genuine eye-witness.

The suggestion that such eye-spots serve to mislead assumes that predators aim at the eye of the victim. The truth of this assumption can be tested. The eye does play an important part as a target for at least two predatory fish. Angler-fish (Antennariidae) (figure 25) suck in their prey with a sudden implosion, and can generally do this only when the head of the victim (another fish) is swallowed first. These fish identify the correct orientation of the victim from its eyes. If fish are presented whose eyes are difficult to discern and are not even located in the normal camouflage stripe, they are sometimes snapped at tail-first and may succeed in escaping by thrusting forwards with all their might. Another predator which aims at the eye of its prey is the sabre-toothed blenny (*Runula*), which bites lumps out of the skin of other fish (as described on page 165). It is thus a valid assumption that the eye of the prey acts as a target for the predator at least in some cases. However, it is also known that eye-spots on the body, particularly on the gill-covers of some freshwater fish, can function as important social signals for conspecifics. This possibility must also be taken into account and it is rather difficult to determine in any given case which function is predominant since the two effects are not mutually exclusive.

Although we know little about the significance of dummy heads, there are some good examples showing that animals really do develop a deceptive dummy head at the wrong end. In this context, 'head' is synonymous with 'anterior end of the animal' – the part leading in locomotion. It is thus the characteristics of the anterior end which are imitated, rather than the head. The first step in this direction can easily be seen from a cat just before it leaps at a mouse. The cat wags the tip of its tail, which is usually attributed to scarcely contained excitement. But if this is true, the cat is unnecessarily risking exposure, and complete control would be preferable. The same tail-wagging can be seen with lions and also in some lizards and snakes. Young wall lizards *Lacerta muralis*, horned Aganud lizards *Phrynocephalus*, 'horned toads' *Phrynosoma*, and some geckos wriggle the tail when stalking prey. Some colubrids and vipers do the same, while Mertens has described the occasional appearance of such behaviour in young crocodiles.

This tail-wagging is not quite as pointless as it appears. An animal lying in wait for or stalking its prey moves as inconspicuously as possible until it is near enough to pounce, and for this, it is necessary to remain unnoticed by the prey. But most animals that are

Figure 13. Many snakes hold their heads fairly still when faced with opponents or prey, while moving the tip of the tail. This diverts the attention of the animal away from the genuine head end. The false head is often conspicuously coloured so that the actual head is not noticed, as shown here in *Cylindrophis rufus*.

preyed on are very suspicious and watch any suspect object in the immediate vicinity, particularly if it moves. As soon as any moving object comes too close, they flee, whereas they will usually remain immobile as long as the suspect object stays beyond a certain distance. It is advantageous for the prey to stay immobile for as long as possible, otherwise it betrays its position. An animal which is slowly and unnoticeably creeping up to its prey can manoeuvre its lethal anterior end within the critical zone while the attention of its prey is still fixed on the predator's wagging tail end, which for the time being remains outside the critical zone. A nervously twitching tail can distract the attention of the prey long enough for the predator to pounce. In such cases, the twitching tail is an imitation of a very vague, possibly dangerous object. Whether or not this should be included as mimicry is a matter of taste.

Tail-twitching in snakes has specialised in two directions. One

Figure 14. This lantern-fly, an unidentified species from Thailand, has a particularly convincing false head. The conspicuous antennae, the black eyes and the black beak are really appendages of the wing tips. The true head can scarcely be seen and is pressed close to the substrate. The lantern-fly appears to jump backwards when disturbed.

led to the development of a rattle in the tail, which amplifies the rustling noise produced by the tail on the ground; the effect is thus independent of the type of substrate. Rapid shaking tail movements occur when the snake feels that it is threatened by an enemy. The tail rattle consists of the terminal scales of previous moults, which remain attached to their predecessors. The rattling of a large rattlesnake when threatened can sometimes be heard up to thirty yards away, and certainly has a deterrent effect on at least some animals. The other direction of specialisation leads to conspicuous coloration of the underside of the tip of the tail. This colour pattern is only exposed when the tail is raised, as in one American midget boa constrictor *Charina bottae* and some coral snakes (*Micrurus*: see figure 24). In these cases, the tail resembles the head, but is no more conspicuous. It is still not clear whether the tail movements function to distract prey or to deceive predators, but at least man is often unable to distinguish the front and hind end at first sight. Even more deceptive are the conspicuous markings on the underside of the tail-tip of otherwise inconspicuously coloured species. For example, the small poisonous colubrid *Maticora intestinalis* and the completely harmless *Cylindrophis rufus* both exhibit a red patch (figure 13). In this case, the tail does not mimic the head; instead, it is simply the end of the body which is marked by colour and movement and thus misleadingly interpreted as the anterior or head end.

There are also snakes whose head and tail ends are equally conspicuously marked, both ends standing out from the rest of the body. When threatened, such snakes usually twitch the tail more vigorously than the head. This is the case, for instance, with small blind-snakes (*Leptotyphlops*, *Typhlops*), referred to by natives in quite separate regions as two-headed snakes, and also with the Ethiopian *Chilorhinops* or the East Asian *Calamaria*.

It would be unwise to talk of head mimicry in these cases until we know more about which animals react and how. We do not even know which end of the body formed the prototype; it could just as well be a case of tail mimicry. In fact it may not be a case of one end mimicking the other. It might simply represent a means to confuse possible enemies which recognise that it is a snake but cannot decide which end is the anterior end. It could also be a mechanism to give the impression of double the number of snakes, since it is not certain that the opponent can recognise that the two ends belong together. This might complicate the decision *which* snake to attack, or even scare the opponent off, if it is unwilling to take on two, possibly poisonous, snakes at once. These possibilities remain unproved. Nevertheless, it appears almost indisputable that the dummy heads are no freak of nature but perform a biological function, involving the deception of another animal. A similar deception can be found in some insects, the best example of which is probably the Siamese lantern-fly illustrated in figure 14. This insect mimics two insect antennae with the tips of its hind-wings and bears a large dummy eye on each fore-wing. The lantern-flies (Fulgoridae) are good jumpers and jump in a direction opposite to that expected from a view of the dummy head.

A little more is known about the dummy head of the hair-streak *Thecla* from Curio's observations in Guayaquil (figure 15). Hair-streaks belong to the 'blues' (Lycaenidae) and derive their name from outgrowths on the hind-wings. These outgrowths may be short and thread-like, or larger than the body, contorted and ribbon-like, as in the East African *Hypolycaena*. Many species, namely those in South America, are extremely colourful. The undersides of the wings of the North American *Strymon melinus* are brown and inconspicuous, but the short tips, which are reminiscent of insect antennae, lie just behind an orange-coloured patch containing a black eye-spot. At a glance, this gives the impression of a head. Curio also observed that the hind ends of the wings of *Thecla togarna* resemble a head. When this butterfly is resting with folded wings, the laterally raised wing edges give a particularly striking impression of hemi-spherical, protruding eyes since white spots above act as pseudo-headlights. The dummy antennae at the wing-tips are broadened and whitish, giving the impression of antennae with shiny end-bulbs. A number of surprising idiosyncracies in behaviour are also present. As soon as it has landed, the butterfly carries out up-and-down movements with the dummy antennae by jerking its hind-wings. The real antennae are kept immobile. While doing this, *Thecla* runs a short distance in the direction of the real head, although a relative, *Deudorix*, runs in the direction of the dummy head. In addition, *Thecla* performs a startling feat at the moment of landing: the butterfly turns very quickly so that the dummy head comes to point in the previous direction of flight. Presumably this deceives predators. In order to catch a squatting butterfly with the beak or with a pair of forceps, it is essential to keep something in reserve in order to counter the expected escape, which is why birds hold back when catching winged insects. This involves knowing which end is the front. Thus, *Thecla togarna* misdirects the reserve counter-action both with its dummy head and with the turnabout on landing.

Figure 15 (*above*). Butterflies of the genus *Thecla* draw attention away from the true head and direct it to an imitation head at the hind end by means of converging colour stripes on the wings and antenna-like appendages on the wing tips. In addition, *Thecla togarna* (above) on landing swings its hind end into the previous direction of flight and subsequently flies off in the opposite direction.

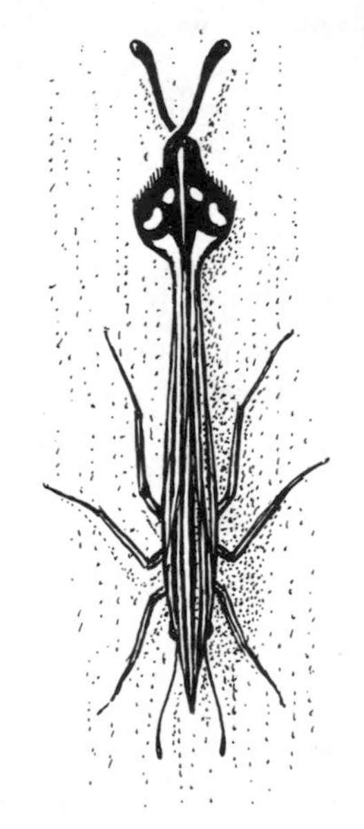

Figure 16 (*right*). The Trinidad species T. *linus* squats on vertical surfaces – presumably with its head always pointing downwards – and moves its wing appendages like antennae.

Related species which squat on vertical stems with the head downwards may be interpreted as showing the first step in this direction, (figure 16) since butterflies usually rest on vertical surfaces with the head uppermost.

Of course, one is free to decide whether or not to accept the interpretation of these peculiarities as protective adaptations. It is not my intention to use these examples as an argument to support a particular theory, but simply to describe the number of adaptations so far discovered which possibly or probably provide protection against predators. One then has a working hypothesis which can be tested. If no such assumption is made, one is left either without a working hypothesis, which means abandoning further research, or one must produce another hypothesis, which must also be tested.

7 Müllerian mimicry

Bates noticed that occasionally two inedible unrelated butterfly species were amazingly similar in appearance. He could not explain this, but an explanation was soon provided, in 1878, by the German zoologist Fritz Müller. Like Bates, Müller observed and caught butterflies in Brazil. He also assumed that animals learn to recognise inedible prey after bad experiences. This means that the inedible animal has to sacrifice a number of individuals to provide the predator with experience. Now if there were a number of inedible species, then the predator would have to learn to recognise each separately. But if the different prey species had the same appearance, and the predator were unable to distinguish between them, then only one type would have to be learned. Put another way, the predator would learn to recognise the particular species with which it happened to have contact and then avoid animals of similar appearance. Thus, the other species of similar appearance would not have to sacrifice further individuals to the predator, and the total number of individuals sacrificed to each predator would be spread over all of the species included in the 'warning club'. The greater the number of species employing the same warning signals, the lower the losses of the individual species. In this way, a plausible solution was provided for Bates' paradox, and soon afterwards a number of Müllerian mimicry-rings were identified. Of course, a Batesian mimic can also belong to a Müllerian mimicry club of this type (figure 18), since the greater the number of species in the Müllerian club, the greater the number of the genuine model.

As with other forms of mimicry, it is difficult to make definitions when it is assumed that species bearing the same warning patterns owe their similarity to a mutual interaction. For example, one would not speak of Müllerian mimicry when animals so different as the spotted salamander, the caterpillars of Cinnabar Moth and hornets all employ the same black-and-yellow warning coloration. These species have developed these patterns independently of one another simply because they have a very strong effect in drawing the attention of possibly very different predators. Most examples of Müllerian mimicry, however, involve different species with the same complex patterns. There are also other difficulties of definition. As mentioned before, Müllerian mimicry increases in efficiency the greater the number of species in the system and the better the correspondence in pattern between the various numbers of the system. Sexual dimorphism should therefore be out of the question, as is the case. What is awkward for the theory, however, is the occurrence of polymorphism in some species, as in *P. dardanus*, but with both sexes equally affected by this. One example is provided by various inedible butterflies in South America, where members of quite different families (Danaidae, Ithomiidae, Acraeidae, Heliconiinae) have closely similar warning patterns. In the Heliconiinae, there are also closely related species which resemble one another. In some cases, there is evidence that the correspondence between several species of the same genus is a secondary feature and they were less similar at an earlier stage of evolution. All this comes under the concept of Müllerian mimicry, but unfortunately the converse also occurs: the species *Heliconius melpomene* and *H. erato* are two of the most variable species known. Each species contains roughly thirty different morphs, each of which forms a pair with a morph of similar appearance from another species. As a rule, these butterflies of parallel appearance co-exist in the same area, but not always. In addition, some of the morphs are non-mimetic. The occurrence of non-mimetic morphs and the presence of different morphs within a mimetic species cannot be explained on the basis of Müllerian mimicry as formulated above.

Attempts have been made to find other causes for this phenomenon. Of course, the colour pattern also plays a part in courtship and is thus important in reproduction. But the species mentioned above all prefer a large predominance of red in the wing-pattern overall, and this speaks against polymorphism. Both colour and odour signals also play a part in mating, as has been described previously for other butterflies. *Heliconius erato* has an innate preference for yellow flowers when hungry and searching for food. During courtship, on the other hand, orange-red is necessary. Uniformly coloured orange-red dummies work better than genuine

Figure 17 (*below*). One unexplained case is that of the correspondence in coloration between various morphs of African shrikes and representatives of related species, which live in the same regions as the corresponding smaller billed morph. Very little is known of the behaviour of these birds. Top: *Malaconotus monteiri* (left) and M. *cruentus* (right). Bottom: the yellow and red morph of *M. multicolor* (females).

Figure 18 (*right*). Examples of Batesian and Müllerian mimicry-rings in butterflies are shown alongside one another in vertical rows. The unpalatable models are above the grey horizontal line, with the mimics below. Batesian mimicry is the similarity between butterflies from above the lines with those from below; Müllerian mimicry is the similarity between butterflies above the line.

Left group (African): from top to bottom, male *Acraea aleiope aurivilli* Staud., female *Planema poggei welsoni* Dewitz, male *Planema macarista* Sharpe, male *Pseudacraea kuenowi* Dewitz alongside male *Precis rauana* Grose Smith, male *Pseudacraea hobleyi* Neave, alongise the large female of *Papilio dardanus planemoides* Trimen.

Middle group (African): from top to bottom, ventral wing surface of *Mylothris agathine* Crm., male *Belonois thysa* Hopff., female *Phrissure phoebe* Butl., and female *Pinacopteryx rubrobasalis* Lanz.

Right group (South American): from top to bottom, *Mechanitis lysimnia*, *Lycorea halia*, *Heliconius eurate*, *Melinaea ethra*, female *Perrhybris pyrrha*, and female *Dismorphia astynome*. The last two species are cabbage-white butterflies.

females, as long as the dummies move. Squatting and flying females attract males in the immediate vicinity with a scent. The female can emit a special warning substance from the everted abdominal glands, in response to being seized, but only after copulation. Crane postulates that this behaviour is derived from the mating behaviour while the red coloration for courtship is derived from the warning coloration. The butterfly certainly tastes bad and is avoided by many predators, from grasshoppers to Rhesus monkeys, though not by some ants and spiders.

The genetics of polymorphism in *Heliconius* has been investigated by experimental crosses, as was done with *Papilio dardanus*, and Turner recently summarised the results. Monomorphic populations of *H. melpomene* and *H. erato* occur at the edges of the ranges of distribution of these species. If butterflies of one species are taken from opposing fringe areas and crossed, the great polymorphic variation typical of the central area is obtained. Various facts indicate that the ranges of the two species were split by climatic barriers in the Pleistocene, so that separate populations of each species developed to give sub-species. When the climate changed, the populations were rejoined and the hybridisation area produced the great variation in the form that we find today. This does not explain why these forms should have been maintained, however; nor does it explain why two species should produce exactly parallel morphs. Although it is known that polymorphism is sometimes controlled by single genes, sometimes by groups of genes, and that switch genes (as explained for *Papilio dardanus*) may also play a part, it is obscure which selective agencies are involved.

Another puzzle is polymorphism in *Heliconius doris*. One widely-distributed green morph of this species is non-mimetic and there is no evidence to indicate that hybridisation has given rise to the polymorphism; there are no living monomorphic populations. This forces the admission that polymorphism in butterflies showing Müllerian mimicry has not been explained, and yet the phenomenon is not necessarily inexplicable since we know too little about the ecology, genetics and evolutionary history of these species.

Basic arguments against Müllerian mimicry

The most important arguments against Müllerian mimicry do not stem from the problems mentioned so far, but from theoretical considerations of the general concept of mimicry.

The Müllerian type of mimicry has the following in common with the Batesian type: different species are strikingly similar in appearance, and unrelated species may be closer in appearance than closely related species. Of course there are cases in Müllerian mimicry of closely related species being similar in appearance, although this is not surprising since they have inherited the same warning coloration from a common ancestor. Species that are closely related are nevertheless quoted as examples of Müllerian mimicry; in fact they provided the first chief witnesses. Even so, this situation has given rise to arguments which have been overlooked by previous theoreticians of mimicry, and concern the problems of relationship and that of the deception of the signal-receiver.

It has already been explained that difficulties arise when one attempts to classify interspecific resemblances as Batesian mimicry. Difficulties also arise with Müllerian mimicry when dealing with intraspecific similarities. Individuals of one species of similar appearance have, of course, carried over their similarity in coloration from a common ancestor; all hornets look alike because they had hornets as parents. In the same way, the hornets (*Vespula crabro*) and the common wasps of the genus *Vespula* are similar in appearance, since they have inherited their black and yellow coloration from a common ancestor with this pattern. Is this all to be called Müllerian mimicry? Logically, such cases of common parentage and ancestry come under Müllerian mimicry, and yet one would scarcely take the wasps or bees within one hive as an example of mimicry. Nevertheless, the main feature in each case is the standardisation of a signal; that is, a signal is made as uniform as possible to convey one meaning. For birds, black-and-yellow rings simply mean 'watch out, inedible!' Any animal which is really inedible benefits most by developing this signal whatever family it belongs to. For a bird, only the signal and its significance are important and not the blood relationship of the signal-transmitters. The question now arises: should the biologist take this into account or classify according to other criteria? If the latter choice is made, it could be required that Müllerian mimetic species should have developed their resemblances independently, that is by convergent evolution. This requirement, of course, does not apply to Batesian mimicry, since it can happen that one of two related, inedible species with commonly inherited similar warning patterns loses its inedible qualities and then depends completely on the other genuinely protected species. This would be a typical case of Batesian mimicry, even though the correspondence in coloration results from a common ancestor. Of course, independent development could be set up as a criterion for Batesian mimicry as well. This latter case produces another difficulty, however. If a species loses its repellant taste, this would occur gradually, and a time must come when two species of similar appearance have different degrees of inedibility. This is not a hypothetical situation; it does exist, even if the evolution of the species concerned is not known in detail. In any case it is scarcely to be expected that two different species should be exactly similar in inedibility. So this would be an example of Müllerian mimicry insofar as both species enjoy protection, and yet at the same time an example of Batesian mimicry because the less protected species is a one-sided dependant upon the stronger.

Batesian and Müllerian mimicry are thus not mutually exclusive; there are all forms of transition between the two, as was emphasised by Darlington in 1938. The same conclusion is reached when one considers the frequency with which the signal-receiver encounters two species of this kind. If one species is encountered more frequently, the other becomes the beneficiary and is therefore a Batesian mimic, assuming that the latter species is not better in defence, more repulsive in taste or otherwise better protected. On the other hand, a rare, extremely repulsive species and a more common, and less repulsive species could be Müllerian partners.

As long as some Batesian mimetic effect exists, the signal-receiver is deceived, however slightly, about the inedibility of one species. In pure Müllerian mimicry, the signal-receiver avoids all members of the warning pattern association with good reason. There is no deception, there is no division into model and mimic, and, bearing the usual definition of mimicry in mind, no mimicry at all. Genuine Müllerian mimicry is thus not mimicry after all.

The last twist in the story has already been briefly mentioned. All members of a defensive or inedible species should bear the same warning coloration. If, for example, some hornets were ringed in black and yellow, while others were white and blue tartan and yet others were covered in silver spots, the predators would have to learn all three colour patterns. The hornets would then have to sacrifice three times as many individuals as when all look alike and where the predator has to learn only one pattern. If differences in warning coloration are senseless when different species are concerned, then it would be even more senseless within one and the same species. But just this ridiculous situation arises in the case of the polymorphic, inedible butterflies of the genus *Heliconius* mentioned previously.

8 Riddle of the long-horned beetle

The Malacodermata, relatives of the fire-flies, are very conspicuous in colour, and this applies especially to those in the sub-family Lycinae. Most are orange and black, or orange and blue, and are peculiar in that the elytra are broader at the tip than at the base; they also sit on open flowers and fly slowly. When danger threatens, the beetles of this group actively eject a foul-smelling fluid from the hind femora. They are avoided by birds and insectivorous mammals, while Linsley, Eisner and Klots state that they are also avoided by Solifuga, mantids, ants and *Polistes* wasps. Shelford described a number of entirely unrelated insects in Borneo, which all resemble Malacodermata, and his list included the bug *Serinetha abdominalis*, which is inedible. He found this bug together with a butterfly of similar form, *Phauda limbata*, both in the Botanical Gardens in Singapore and in Sarawak. Both insects may sit together on plant stems. The long-horned beetle *Erythrus rotundicollis* also resembles the same bug, but it is not known if the beetle is inedible.

It is interesting to note that a parallel resemblance series from just the same groups of insects, though from different genera, is to be found in South Africa (figure 19). This series, which was described by Wallace, includes a Malacodermatoid beetle, a bug, a butterfly and a Longicorn beetle. In addition, there is a further member in the form of an independently protected wasp. Various southern areas of the United States also show corresponding mimicry rings. According to Linsley, Eisner and Klots, these rings consists of the following species:

1. The Lycids *Lycus fernandezi* and *L. arizonensis*, the butterflies *Seryda constans* (Pyromorphidae). *Ptychoglene coccinea* and *P. phrada* (Lithosiidae) and the Longicorn beetle *Elytroleptus apicalis*.
2. The Lycids *Lycus loripes* and *L. simulans*, the butterflies *Eubaphe unicolor* (Geometridae) and *Holomelina ostentata* (Arctiidae) and the Longicorn beetle *Elytroleptus ignitus*. *Holomelina* is inedible in its own right, so it provides together with the Lycids an example of Müllerian mimicry, while the other insects represent Batesian mimics.

Longicorn beetles are very famous as mimics. Beetles of this group resemble wasps, bees, ants and quite unrelated, inedible beetles. In some cases, closely related Longicorn beetles are completely different in size, shape and coloration, and resemble entirely different models. That mimicry is involved here seems strikingly apparent to an observer.

On the island of Cuba, there is a group that contains different beetles which closely resemble each other and also the animals depicted in figure 19. The group includes three Lycid species (*Thonalmus suavis*, *T. aulicus*, *T. amabilis*), three Cantharid species (*Tytthonyx rubidus*, *T. rutilis*, *T. darlingtoni*), an Oedemerid (*Copidita thonalmus*), two Elaterids (*Anaplischius venustus*, *Platycrepidius schaumi*) and six Cerambycids or Longicorn beetles (*Calocosmus venustus*, *C. dimidiatus*, *Trichrous divisus*, *T. pilipennis*, *T. dimidiatipennis*, *Heterops dimidiata*). Darlington carried out experiments with these insects and a number of possible predators. He found that lizards of the genus *Anolis* kept in captivity would touch neither the Lycids nor the Oedemerids, both of which are regarded as protected. In addition, Longicorn beetles resembling four different Lycid species were also ignored, even when left in the cage for a week. In contrast, beetles of various families and Longicorn beetles of the same size that were differently coloured were eaten in large numbers in the course of the test. Longicorn beetles regarded as being mimetic should really be introduced directly into the lizard's mouth in order to exclude the possible influence of the colour as an optical stimulus. In this way, it could be determined whether this is a case of Müllerian or Batesian mimicry. It must be one of the two, according to Darlington, since none of the *Thonalmus*-like beetles could possibly be a predator on Lycids. This, however, is a mistaken assumption; Eisner, Kafatos and Linsley recently demonstrated an amazing situation existing among the Lycid-like Longicorn beetles.

On a meadow near a research station in Arizona, the Lycids *Lycus loripes* and *L. fernandezi* live alongside the Longicorn beetles *Elytroleptus ignitus* and *E. apicalis*. *L. loripes* and *E. ignatus* are unformly coloured light orange; the other two species are basically

Figure 19. The parallel mimicry-rings from South Africa (upper row) and Borneo (lower row) show a high degree of correspondence. Upper row: from left to right, male and female of the soft-shelled beetle *Lycus rostratus*, the longicorn beetle *Amphidesmus analis*, the bug *Lygaeus fureatus*, the butterfly *Neurosymploca ochreipennis*, and the spider-wasp *Pompilus capensis*. Lower row: from left to right, male and female of the soft-shelled beetle *Lycostomus gestroi*, the male longicorn beetle *Erythrus rotundicollis*, the bug *Serinetha abdominalis*, and the butterfly *Phauda limbata*.

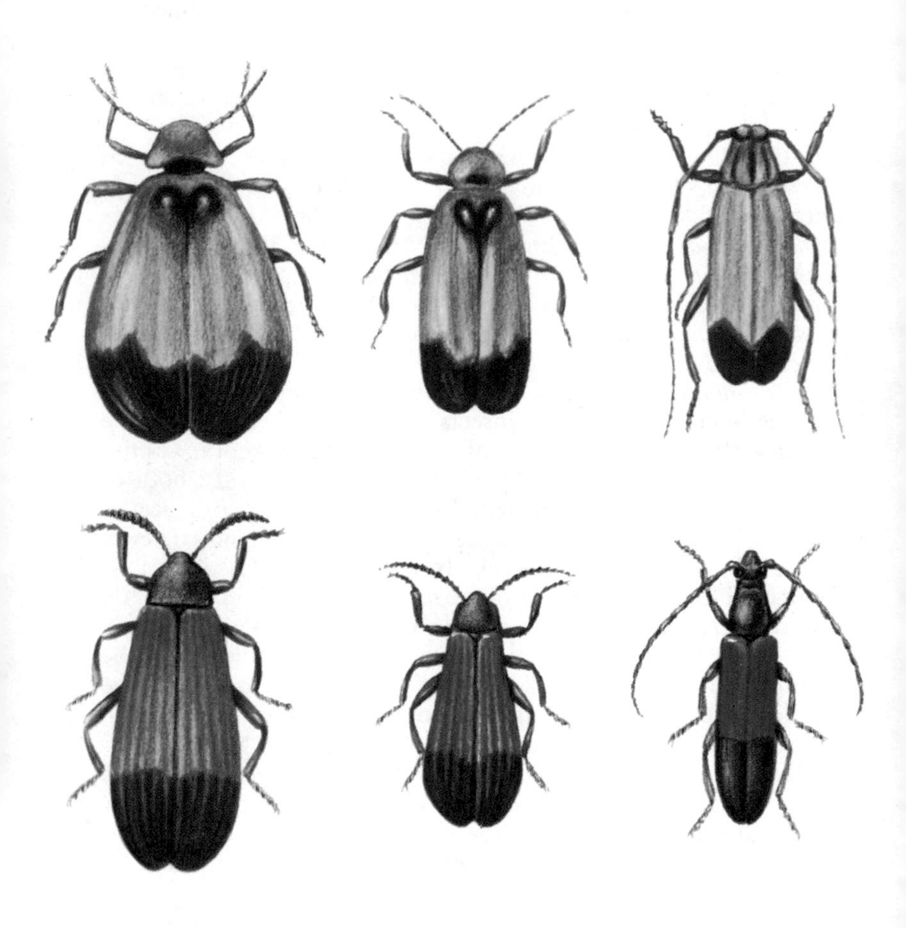

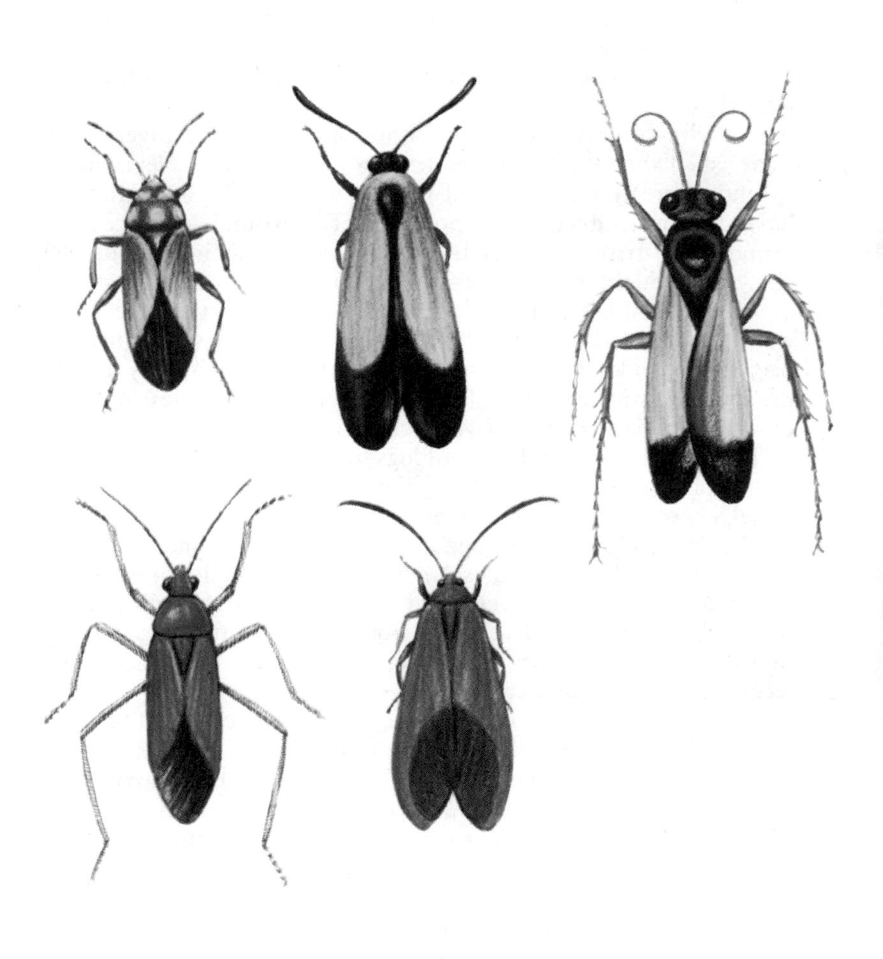

similar, but the elytra have black tips. The correspondence of each Longicorn beetle with the appropriate Lycid species is amazingly exact. The Longicorn beetles are far less common, there being roughly one to every hundred Lycid individuals. A series of experiments with several insectivores, both vertebrate and invertebrate, established that the Lycid beetles are also inedible. Nevertheless, wounds were found on Lycid beetles with all the appearance of having been produced by a predator. The wounds are frequently found at the bases of the elytra, which were sometimes completely chewed through. A closer examination showed that the wounds could not have been caused by birds. The form of the edges of the wounds indicated that an arthropod, possibly an insect, must have been responsible. Patient observation in the field eventually revealed the evil-doers in the form of the two Longicorn species. A Longicorn beetle, on meeting a Lycid, climbs on to its back, holding on with the front and middle pair of legs to the elytra of the victim. The Longicorn beetle holds on to a plant with the hind legs, palpates the elytra of the victim and then begins to bite. Blood immediately exudes from the small wounds produced, and is imbibed by the Longicorn beetle. Sometimes, the predacious Longicorn bites open the thorax of the other beetle and devours the large flight muscles. Strangely enough, the Lycids do not defend themselves; the most that they do is to attempt to escape, whereupon the Longicorn may let go and the wounds seem to heal. At other times the Longicorn eats away the elytra, maybe with a leg or two, and completely empties the thoracic cavity in about half an hour. This is the first evidence that any of the Longicorn beetles may be predators, apart from unreliable reports of spider-hunting by the European musk-beetle. The two species of Longicorns do not confine themselves to their respective Lycids, however; the related Lycid species are also attacked. It is therefore unlikely that the similarity between predator and prey serves to confuse the latter, as with aggressive mimicry (page 122). In fact the victim probably does not have an opportunity to perceive the pattern of the predator. Other experiments show that the two Longicorn species are edible and that they

Figure 20. Soft-shelled beetles and longicorn beetles of very similar appearance can also be found in America. So much is known about these insects that it is now impossible to fit them into either of the classical types of mimicry. The longicorn beetles (here *Elytroleptus ignitus*) partially or completely eat soft-shelled beetles (here *Lycus loripes*). However, the resemblance between the two is not necessary for this behaviour.

are actually eaten by insectivores, at least as long as the latter have had no experience with the inedible Lycids. But this is equally remarkable, since it means that the repulsively tasting body fluid taken up by the Longicorn from the Lycid must be broken down quite rapidly. In all probability, the speed of breakdown is not all that great so that the Longicorn must taste just as repulsive as the Lycids for a period of time. In this way, the predatory beetle has come to be an alternating example of both Batesian and Müllerian mimicry, depending on its appetite at any given time.

This case, first elucidated in 1962, is a further example of the principle that it is better to conduct observations than to argue about terminology. One should now consider whether predator-prey relationships of this kind apply to the many instances where Longicorn beetles resemble Lycids in various tropical and subtropical regions. Nobody has yet investigated this, and it is still not clear which animals act as signal-receivers for the Lycid-like coloration of the Longicorn beetles. The practice of the latter in eating away at Lycids is similar to the introductory copulatory behaviour performed on the back of Longicorn females, where the male performs biting actions on the thorax and elytra of the female. In addition, various male Malacodermoid beetles of the Lycid group produce a secretion from the elytra to provide the females with a chewing stimulus during copulation. Perhaps misunderstood or misused components of mating behaviour play a part in the Longicorn-Lycid relationship, but it is not known how far coloration is involved in the recognition of conspecifics.

9 Experimental investigations

A number of Darlington's experiments have already been mentioned on the relationship between Malacodermoid and Longicorn beetles. Darlington considered his experiments to be rather inconclusive, since too little is known of the normal habits of the animals investigated. This goes for both the beetles and the predaceous lizards. In experiments it is essential to investigate the possibility of learning in predators, and whether they avoid particular prey on the basis of past experience. Experiments on animals whose past experience is unknown are unreliable; predators should be examined whose past history is known – in other words, artificially reared, inexperienced animals must be used. And in order to be quite sure of the right results, the animals should be allowed to reach adulthood before testing them with the models and mimics under investigation. It is well known from behavioural research that some innate reactions only mature at a given age, so that a cursory examination of juvenile animals might give the impression that the reactions involved must be learnt. If the necessary safety precautions are taken, all attempts to train various animals to recognise the significance of warning signals, including artificial patterns, meet with reasonable success. Experiments of this kind have been repeatedly made, and a few will be dealt with now.

Jane van Zandt Brower employed the jay *Cyanocitta coerulescens* from Florida as a predator in a number of experimental series using the following butterflies:

MODELS		MIMICS	
Danaidae	*Danaus plexippus*	Nymphalidae	*Limenitis archippus*
Papilionidae	*Battus philenor*	Papilionidae	*Papilio troilus* and *P. polyxenes*
Danaidae	*Danaus gilippus berenice*	Nymphalidae	*Limenitis archippus floridensis*

Inexperienced birds ate *Limenitis archippus* without hesitation. They also took the first *Danaus plexippus* which was offered, but they showed a strong aversive reaction and ceased biting. In succeeding encounters with the model, the birds showed a decreasing tendency to bite and soon abandoned this response altogether. Afterwards, when *Limenitis* was presented, it was also ignored. Both butterflies have an orange ground-colour with black and white markings. The same result was obtained with *Battus* and the two *Papilio* mimics; the birds ignored Battus after the first unpleasant encounter. In this case, however, three of the jays proved able to distinguish between model and mimic and avoided only the model. It is therefore unwise to base conclusions about a species and its selective effect on observations of a single animal. The third series of experiments showed an unexpected result: some birds, which were acquainted with *Danaus plexippus* from the first series, avoided the mimic *Liminitis archippus floridensis* without prior experience of the model *Danaus gilippus*, apparently because this mimic was confused with the far less similar model *D. plexippus*. This shows that even superficial similarities can have a protective effect. Further experiments with other birds and butterflies confirmed this conclusion. This provided a convincing argument in support of the hypothesis that a mimic can be slowly perfected by a process of evolution, enjoying degrees of protection while still perfecting the similarity. Examples of poor resemblances and artificial mimicry tests give the same results, and yet the opinion is frequently expressed that a mimic must show perfect correspondence to the model in order to enjoy protection. According to this view, the mimic must either fall from the sky ready-made, since nature never proceeds in large leaps, or be propelled past the first, disadvantageous stages of mimicry by some mysterious force. Brower in 1963 also carried out more extensive experiments and tested examples of Müllerian mimicry in neotropical butterflies. She was able to demonstrate that members of a Müllerian mimicry ring show various degrees of distastefulness, thus acting as mutual models of varying effectiveness.

In all these experiments the bird showed different levels of response: not touching the insect, brief pecking, killing and eating. In each experiment, the bird also received an edible butterfly in order to test its readiness to eat, which was placed randomly before or after the test butterfly so that the bird would not become adapted to a particular order of presentation. In 1965 Brower carried out similar experiments on the terrestrial toad *Bufo terrestris*, this time working together with her husband. The bumble-bee *Bombus americanorum* or the bee robber-flie *Mallophora bomboides* and the bees *Apis mellifica* or the hover-flie *Eristalis vinetorum* were offered, the flies being the mimics in each case. After a few encounters the toads learnt very rapidly to avoid bees and bumble-bees; they did not even attempt to bite on seeing them and usually left the mimics alone as well. A number of toads still avoided bees without further training after a period of three months. The toads learnt nothing from bees whose sting had been removed; they were eaten without any hesitation. *Mallophora* is a fly that lays its eggs in the nests of bumble-bees and parasitises them. It is not known whether its resemblance to the bee is also helpful in this role.

Experiments have also been carried out to determine the most effective warning colours. Mealworms were used in a number of investigations, and those which were to act as models were embittered with quinine solution, while those intended as mimic were not treated. The models and the untreated worms were then painted with similar coloured strips and offered to insectivorous birds. As might be expected, conspicuous colour patterns were learnt most rapidly. This method can also be used as a means of investigating the numerical proportions between models and mimics. Brower (1960) fed starlings with normal mealworms, two segments of which were painted orange. Other mealworms were made distasteful and the same two segments were marked with green. A third category included normal, untreated worms with the same two segments coloured green. There is no known case in nature where green functions as a warning colour and orange as a harmless signal, and so the possibility of any innate reaction entering the experiment was avoided. The tested birds also learnt their task rapidly, as expected, and soon avoided all green-coloured mealworms, whether they were distasteful or not. This entire category was even avoided when 60 per cent edible and 40 per cent distasteful mealworms were presented. This means that the numbers of mimics can definitely exceed the numbers of models if the correspondence is good between them; the protective function does not disappear. Even when the test animals received only 10 per cent distasteful and 90 per cent 'good' mealworms, 17 per cent of the mimics were avoided. This is certainly better than 0 per cent and would provide a species with a certain advantage, assuming that the results can be applied to natural conditions. Almost all the test birds made mistakes now and then and pecked once at the model, but it was also observed that a bird would sometimes spit out a mimic which it had taken into its mouth, indicating that a hasty response had been tempered by subsequent consideration. Reiskind (1965) carried out the same experiments with willow tits *Parus atricapillus*, which were presented with normal and artificially embittered sunflower seeds in two parallel experimental series, using green and orange respectively as the warning colour. The same results were obtained: the animals hesitated longer when presented with mimics than when presented with normal seeds, which in the wild would provide a threatened mimic with a good chance of escaping. Mimic seeds which had already been taken up were spat out again.

Duncan and Sheppard (1965) imitated the conditions of Batesian mimicry in the following way: chickens were offered water coloured in different shades of green, instead of being presented with normal prey. The darkest water served as the model, and if the chicken chose this it was punished with an electric shock. All the lighter shades of water represented the mimics and could be drunk without punishment. The animals soon learnt to avoid dark green, and the quantity of water drunk varied inversely with the intensity of the green colour. This result demonstrates that even incomplete mimicry provides a degree of protection. In addition, parallel experiments were conducted, in which the two experimenters used either a weak or a strong electric shock as punishment. Animals which received a strong shock with the dark green water drank only from the very light solutions, although the adjacent weakly-coloured solutions were completely free from punishment stimuli. Translated into the language of mimicry, this means that in the presence of mild punishment, the selective advantage increases progressively with the degree of resemblance, thus leading to a maximum degree of resemblance; in the presence of severe punishment, improvements in resemblance do not bring any advantage above a certain level.

By this stage the reader may have noticed that similar experiments can be extracted from the abundant literature on conditioned stimuli. It is well known that animals can be trained to connect various activities with signals of widely varying types that take the form of reward or punishment. Numerous experiments have been carried out to determine the optimum time interval between the punishable activity and the punishing stimulus, the dependence of the speed of learning upon the strength of the punishing or rewarding stimulus, the various possibilities for rewarding and punishing, how long the animal remembers in the absence of training, reward or punishment, and so forth. The details of such investigations can, for example, be found in Hull (1943). Such investigations support the results already mentioned. The acquisition of conditioned reflexes is such a common feature in the lives of animals that such results can be quite reasonably extended in principle to mimicry. The objection that animals can be trained to react to a wide range of stimuli, but that we do not know whether such factors play a role in mimicry, is naturally something to be looked into in any new experiments on mimicry. Nevertheless, this objection seems rather pointless, unless it is supposed to provoke people to make observations under natural conditions.

The assertion that experiments on caged birds and butterflies are invalid stubbonly appears in the literature. It is maintained that birds do not eat butterflies, this being an opinion which is partly based on the indirect argument that butterflies with bite-marks on the wings are too rarely found. This statement is made in the face of the fact that collections of butterflies exist where bite-marks can be seen symmetrically on both wings, which rules out the possibility that the marks were caused by the butterfly scraping against obstacles. Another argument is based on the statement that no one has seen birds catch butterflies in the wild and that bird stomachs never contain butterfly remains. Birds must be known in detail, however, before a negative statement of this kind can be confidently made. In any case, this statement is invalidated by observations carried out by G. O. H. Carpenter and other field-workers. In one instance Carpenter observed in East Africa two white wagtails hunting close to a spring in blinding sunshine. The two birds devoured something like fifty butterflies in the short space of fifteen minutes. On another occasion, he observed one animal devour twelve butterflies within ten minutes. Recently, birds were observed to prey on peppered moths in England. These birds are very easily disturbed, so they must be observed from a hide. When this was done, it was found that thrushes noticed butterflies on tree-trunks while moving around on the ground and picked them off; similarly, robins keep a lookout from twigs and ferns, yellow-hammers hover around close to a tree-trunk and look for butterflies, and so on. The capture of the prey takes place so rapidly that it is understandable why the first official observation was made only in 1953. Even after this, many naturalists remained sceptical, but a number of these were finally convinced by a film which Professor Tinbergen had taken from the hide.

10 Ant mimics

Since so many insects and spiders look like ants, the concept of ant mimicry is a long established one, and yet the significance of the various similarities is in most cases unknown. Wasmann provided an extensive catalogue of examples of these up to 1925. Since then, little has been added. The main question as to whether ants are protected usually receives a negative answer, at least as far as birds are concerned. It remains to be seen whether there are other ant predators which seek the ants by sight. There is little basis for believing that ant mimicry provides protection against predators, and there is just as little reason to believe that an animal camouflaged as an ant can creep up on its prey more easily. What effect does the resemblance have, then? Followers of the protective pattern school who have examined this question maintain that this is not mimicry in its restricted sense, but mimesis. It is postulated that the ant mimics simply wish to remain unnoticed, to disappear among ants. Nevertheless, one supposes that they have a reason for living together with ants. In some cases, it is certainly true that the mimics merge into the company of ants. Finally, there is the question of which animal is affected by the resemblance.

The similarity of animals to ants covers size, coloration, body structure and behaviour. The size is the least decisive factor, since spiders and various insects come in all sizes. One feature of coloration is particularly striking in that the supposed mimics appear to have a waist – the thin stem joining the thorax and the abdomen in ants. A sham stem created by shading is also seen in wasp mimics. Such a deception might affect optically oriented organisms. Similarities also occur where behaviour is concerned. Some spiders look deceptively like ants and run together with ants through the undergrowth. Spiders have eight legs and ants six, and so the spiders run with only six legs and use the front pair to probe in front of them, as the ants do with their antennae. However, some other non-mimicking spiders move in the same manner. Some ant-like spiders belong to the family Salticidae (jumping spiders) and betray their real identity to an onlooker when they suddenly leap and disappear from a twig, trailing a safety-thread behind them. In many cases where an insect looks like an ant, the insect's body structure differs markedly from that of its close relatives. Yet this need not necessarily be meant to deceive the optical sense of some other animal. Wasmann and other investigators believe that this is a case of 'tactile mimicry' because such insects are found as co-inhabitants of ant societies, and the inner chambers of the nest are completely dark.

It is naturally important to know what drives these insects to enter the nests of ants. Some presumably use the nests for protection and are scarcely noticed by the ants; others are actually tended. In general, the guests must be tolerated by the ants, but this does not neccessarily mean that they must resemble ants. For example, the clavigers (*Clavigerinae*) bear no resemblance to ants whatsoever and secrete a volatile substance which is licked away avidly by the ants. All the same, it is easy to find various guests in ant nests that are more or less similar to their hosts in appearance. Presumably, the similarity facilitates the guest-host relationship, although this conclusion is again purely theoretical. Some species of ant guest are even defended and fed by the ants. On the other hand, some insects resembling ants live within the society of ants and devour their hosts. This latter case would seem to be a case of aggressive mimicry (page 122) although once again examples can be provided where the same ends are achieved without the aid of mimicry. As yet, no investigation of the part played by the nest-odour by which ant compatriots might recognise one another has been carried out.

The survey provided by Wasmann in 1925 to cover the actual phenomena of ant mimicry is exemplary. He made the following list.
1. Genuine guest relationships (symphily), both with and without similarity to ants, where optical or tactile mimicry, or both, may play a part. An example is that of the club-beetles mentioned above. Most of these ant guests live in the nests, although the Lycaenid caterpillars which fall under this heading presumably live outside. It is possible that some tree-hoppers (Membracidae) are also ant guests.
2. Indifferently tolerated sub-tenants. Similarity to ants may be

Figures 21 and 22. It is well known that ants 'milk' aphids by vibrating their antennae against the aphid's back (top). Aphids secrete droplets of honey-dew which are eaten by the ants, in this case by red wood-ants. It was realised recently that this amicable relationship is the result of a misunderstanding: ants normally feed each other, and the ant mistakes the hind end of the aphid (bottom left) for the head end of another ant (bottom right).

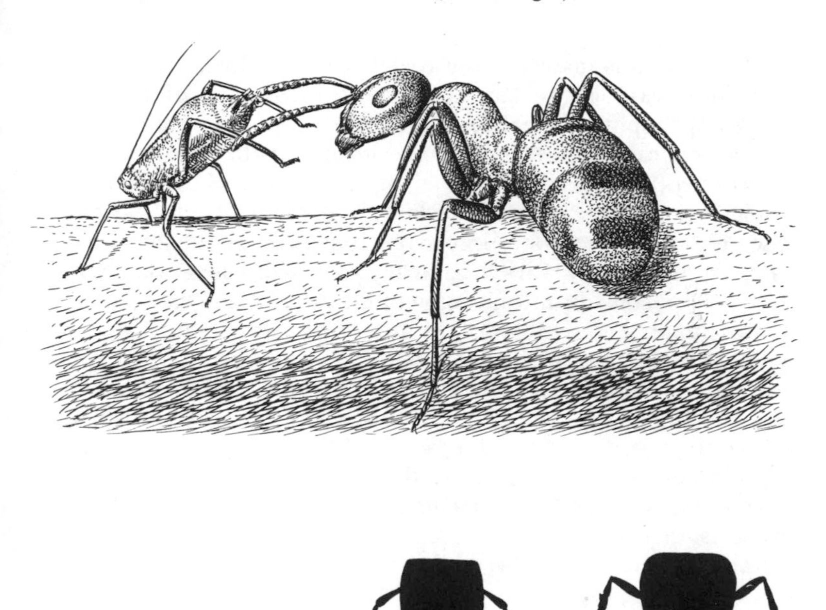

lacking or be represented by hair, coloration or shape.

3. Lodgers attracting hostile pursuit. These can likewise show presence or absence of similarity to ants as regards body structures. Some bugs or spiders also belong to this group.

4. Parasites with or without similarity to ants.

5. Ant associates acting as nutrient donors (trophobionts). These will be dealt with shortly.

The beetle family Staphylinidae provides examples of almost all of these types of association. Seevers (1965) has provided a comprehensive list of the morphological peculiarities and oddities of the Hemipterous insects living together with soldier ants. Particularly impressive is the fact that members of each of the twelve groups of Staphylinid beetles which resemble ants have developed a stem separating thorax from abdomen and they have done this independently. Yet it is still a mystery what these and other similarities to ants actually achieve. In spite of the impressive assembly of facts, we still know precious little about the relationships of these very varied animal types with ants, the sensory stimuli important in mutual communication or the categorisation of the adaptive resemblance to ants. This being the case, a detailed investigation of the Staphylinidae would presumably be the best way to finding answers to these questions. We will see from other examples later on which details would be important in such an investigation.

In the case of ant mimicry, the signal-receiver for which the deception is intended is either unknown or, if we assume that it is the ants themselves which are deceived, has been insufficiently investigated. Up till now, the proponents of ant mimicry have based their arguments on circumstantial evidence and mimicry is taken as the most plausible explanation for the ant-like appearance of animals which live together with ants and look entirely different from their close relatives. Also, the guests of ants with good visual powers (*Eciton* species) actually correspond to ants in colour and shape, while guests of the blind Dorylinae agree only with their hosts in tactile features. Nevertheless, opinion is divided on whether such correlations are conclusive.

The importance of knowing the reactions of the deceived signal-receiver was shown in the case of the trophobionts. Trophobiont is Wasmann's name for insects which serve, not as prey, but as a source of nutrient in the form of sugary secretion. The most famous case is that of the aphids. Few would regard aphids as ant mimics. They do not look like ants at all. They are much smaller and have an entirely different mode of locomotion, or remain virtually immobile. However, Kloft, who has taken a closer look at the behaviour of ants towards aphids, regards this opinion as wrong. He concludes that the ant-aphid relationship is actually a very good demonstration of an original misunderstanding on the part of the ant, a misunderstanding which may even provide the main basis for the present-day relationship. He maintains that ants regard aphids as fellow ants without the aphids being able to do anything about it. To this extent, Wasmann's statement that there is no known case of adaptive resemblance to ants among trophobionts still holds. A firmly-settled aphid which is sucking sap from a plant is palpated at the hind end by ants, in the same way that one ant palpates another. The aphid then gives a response which is very similar to that of an ant stimulated in this way, as long as one remembers that the hind end of the aphid corresponds to the anterior end of an ant (figure 21). Ants beg from one another with extraordinary frequency and the ant which is thus approached will feed the begging ant with a droplet of liquid nutrient from the so-called crop. Since this distributes the food of an ant society fairly evenly among its members, we use the term 'social stomach'. This reciprocal feeding, which is presumably derived from parental care behaviour, forms the bond which holds the entire society together. Ants regularly greet one another by using elements of the feeding behaviour, and it is at first not clear which of the partners will eventually allow itself to be fed. Sometimes, one will try to force its nutrient droplet upon another ant, although this is unsuccessful if the latter is already satiated. When ants run around on their accustomed pathways through the undergrowth and on plants, they now and again encounter the hind end of an aphid. This receives a friendly greeting, since the ant mistakes it for the front end of a colleague. The palpation of the back end of the aphid with the antennae elicits disturbance behaviour on the part of the aphid; it raises its hind legs and produces trampling movements. The ant, however, takes this to be the expected antennal palpations of its presumed colleague. When the greeted aphid eventually secretes a drop of honey-dew, the ant even receives the expected food gift. Kloft was able to elicit exactly the same begging, or greeting, behaviour with dummies. In fact, dummies made from simple round or oval wax lumps had no effect, but the simple addition of two lateral bristles elicited begging in hungry ants (figure 22).

If it is really true that ants regard aphids as conspecifics because the aphid's hind end and its appendages happen by chance to bear a close similarity to the head of an ant, then it should also be the case that ants attempt to feed the aphids. Kloft looked into this carefully and found that this was indeed the case. Satiated ants attempt to favour the hind end of an aphid with a food droplet, although this is of course unsuccessful. These observations are surely a strong argument in favour of the 'confusion theory'.

So far, there is no evidence that the aphids have changed their structure or behaviour in the course of evolution to resemble ants more closely. More likely is the theory that by chance they happen to offer a skeleton key which fits into the social response systems of the ant. The ants defend their aphids against enemies of various kinds, for example against lady-bird larvae. Actually, ants only attack aphid predators when the latter enter ant territories, which include stems that bear aphids. Predators which hatch out of eggs within this territory are accepted and remain unmolested, as was shown by Bänsch. This means that other animals, which need not appear similar to ants, can be accepted in the territory, but they are not greeted or fed. It is not yet known how far ants have altered their social behaviour, originally directed solely towards conspecifies, as an adaptation to the care of aphids. The aphids only exploit this behaviour of the ants in so far as they enjoy protection. Lilac trees, for example, usually bear only a few branches which are traversed by ants, and only the colonies of aphids sitting on these branches are free from predators. The ants, on the other hand, draw benefit from the malfunction of their social behaviour in that they obtain large quantities of sugary sap. Aphids visited by ants produce far more honey-dew than non-visited aphids, and a single society of the red wood-ant *Formica rufa* consumes over 100 kilograms of honey-dew a year. So ants, by their social behaviour, may become pests.

11 The evolution of mimicry

It might appear highly improbable that aphids elicit a reaction from ants so advantageous to both parties just by chance. Yet is such a phenomenon astounding or is it to be expected? If we consider the large number of different species and the wide range of possible relationships between them and with their environments, chance similarities must surely be expected. In fact, there are numerous examples of unintentional functional interference in the evolution of animals and plants, and it would be instructive to mention a few examples. The Labiate plant catmint *Nepeta cataria* has a peculiar effect upon cats. Judging from its colloquial names (Katzenkraut in German), the connection has been known for a long time, but proper investigation was carried out only recently by Palen and Goddard. Cats of both sexes, including castrated cats, react to this plant with quite specific behaviour patterns – rubbing the face, body-rolling – normally performed by a receptive female in the presence of a male. All other aspects of the cat's behaviour remain unchanged and no other sexual behaviour patterns can be elicited in this way. However, the reaction does not appear to help either the cat or the plant. Another example is provided by the nauplius larvae of the marine copepod *Tigriopus californicus*. After a minimum of two hours exposure to high water pressure, those larvae that would normally become males are so altered that they grow into females. The small crustacean normally inhabits small rock-pools at the extreme edge of the tidal zone and so does not naturally encounter such pressures. A response is thus available or possible which is not normally exploited, but could be if a different situation were to arise. Our final example is the bug *Pyrrhocoris apterus*, which is bred in large quantities for laboratory experiments and has recently soared to fame. This bug was first bred in Czechoslovakia but attempts to breed it in America failed. It was then found that the fault lay with the old newspapers used to line the breeding chambers. Certain kinds of paper contain a substance which has a similar effect to that of the juvenile hormone. The bugs therefore remain larvae or develop into forms that look like larvae and die before achieving sexual maturity. The most active papers were the *New York Times*, the *Boston Globe*, the *Wall Street Journal*, the *Scientific American* and *Science* – all prepared mainly from the American balsam fir. The London *Times*, *Nature* and European or Japanese papers were inactive. In the meantime, numerous physiological articles have appeared purporting to explain the basis of this phenomenon.

Substances which attract insects have recently received particular attention. Some of these substances have been used for pest control, by eliminating the males and thus the entire pest population. One success was the attraction of males of the oriental fruit-fly with methyl-eugenol (4-allyl-veratol), which operates like a sexual attractant. Poisoned cardboard fragments were soaked with this substance and then distributed over the 33 square miles of a large island by aeroplane. The pests were exterminated in six months. A man wearing a furry parka with the hood up incorporates the major optical characters of a wolf; in both cases, a reindeer sees a furry mound from the front. Since hunting wolves hold the head lowered, a reindeer flees on seeing a lowered head, but not on seeing the head raised. The human being can elicit the same behaviour by raising or lowering the furry hood, a fact which some hunters exploit. Various bacteria, fungi, thread-worms, mites and insects produce substances which may cause gall-formation in young, growing plant tissues. Substances promoting or inhibiting growth and altering the permeability of the host's cells to water may also be produced. The changes may have no significance for the parasite, but the plant may produce complicated protective and nutritive layers of fruit-like fleshy tissue, which supports the parasite. An inter-relationship between two rotifer species discovered by Beauchamp in 1952 and recently further investigated by Gilbert has all the appearances of a special equilibriated system. Both species occur in the same areas and *Brachyonus calicyflorus* is frequently preyed upon by an *Asplanchna* species. But *Asplanchna* continually exudes a substance into the water that affects *Brachyonus* eggs. The exuded substance, which only affects undeveloped eggs, stimulates the development into a rotifer with two long spines, in addition to the normal three short ones. The extra spines are mobile and spread out when the rotifer contracts. Quite apart from the fact that this substance affects the undivided egg (a very unusual occurrence in animals), and that a different species is affected at a distance from the producer, the reaction is amazing in that the spines produced on the *Brachyonus* actually protect the rotifer against the predatory *Asplanchna*. *Brachyonus* does not have this effect in areas where *Asplanchna* does not occur. Naturally, such influences can lead to the dependence of one species on another, as is found in parasites. The most extreme example of this is the rabbit flea *Spilopsyllus cuniculi*, investigated by Rothschild. This flea reproduces only on pregnant rabbits because the functioning of the germinal cells of the flea are regulated by the sexual hormones of the host. In this way, the reproduction of host and parasite is synchronised so that the young fleas hatch to meet the young rabbits. This is the only example so far discovered where one animal permits its reproductive cycle to be controlled by another. The dependence is so close that the flea will resorb its eggs if the female host miscarries.

Various plants successfully trap insects, although they gain nothing from the victims. Insects up to three millimetres in length often stick to the slimy, adhesive cap of the lamellar-fungus *Hygrophorus eburneum*. Even groups of normal butterflies stick to the spike-panicle of the East African Sticky Grass *Setaria verticillata*. Wingless insects often hide from the light in the leaf-sheaths surrounding the stems of the teasel *Dipsacus silvester*. When the small cup fills with water in a sudden shower it becomes very slippery and many insects drown, particularly hover-flies and parasitic flies (Syrphidae and Tachinidae respectively). This has the appearance of a preliminary stage in the evolution of the pitcher-plants, which are professional insect trappers and digest them.

Many of these chance associations are not exploited by either party, but other relationships develop special adaptations in which one of the parties gains a distinct advantage. This can even take place within the lifetime of a single animal. Some animals learn to make use of experience, including situations where other animals are deceived. For example, thrushes learn to chase competitors into hiding with the warning call for the presence of aerial predators so that they can devour various titbits in peace. Ravens show pronounced submission to hated rivals, including human beings, until the latter approach close enough to be met with an unexpected assault. This unfair behaviour shows that even lying is not a peculiar feature of man. The arctic skua feeds largely on prey wrested from other gulls and terns. Apparently this is facilitated by the similarity between the silhouette of a flying arctic skua and that of a falcon, since the victims let go of their prey before the skua has really begun to harass them; and sandpipers react to skuas in the same way as to falcons. It is not certain whether the skuas learn to exploit this scaring effect, which is presumably partly due to confusion with predators, or whether the effect is firmly incorporated in the skua's instinctive behaviour. The counterpart to this bird – a predatory bird with cryptic protection – is mentioned on page 123.

Without presupposing the results of closer investigations, cases such as these must provide some information about the origins of mimicry. One has to look for origins somewhere, because mimics do not arise ready-made. But difficulties crop up as soon as attempts are made to define mimicry. In general, we use the term mimicry only when the mimetic characters have been evolved for a specific mimetic function. In so doing, it is often forgotten that mimetic characters work only in the presence of definite behaviour patterns, and that a complex of mimetic characters usually incorporates behaviour patterns which are more ancient than the anatomical features. This framework of definition can then give rise to the dilemma that only a single supplementary character may possibly be covered by the concept of mimicry. It is also possible that a character important in mimicry may have arisen to perform an entirely different function and then have altered its function at a later date. Should this be excluded from the concept of mimicry simply because the mimetic character existed previously? We are also faced with the problem of mimetic characters which may have developed additional functions so that the mimetic role becomes the least important. Should we exclude the similarity between aphids and ants from the concept of mimicry just because aphids have always looked the same? At this point, a new element enters the argument, once again because in many cases the signal receiver and its response are not known. In such cases, attempts are made to interpret otherwise inexplicable features of the mimic on the basis of a selective advantage necessary for their evolution. This may well be a practical basis for analysis, but this does not justify us in making it a main criterion for mimicry. If the argument is continued logically, we eventually arrive at virtually insoluble problems, since every character must have origins and predecessors of some kind. As long as such characters do not show a mimetic effect, they cannot be selected to resemble the model more closely, but according to the definition, these characters cannot be mimetic until they have been selected for closer similarity to the model.

Another criterion of mimicry which has been proposed is that the mimetic effect must be more recent than the model. This argument is particularly crass when applied to the leaf-like appearance of many grasshopper species, the extreme case being the walking leaf *Phyllium*. It is claimed that this cannot be a case of leaf mimicry, since Handlirsch has found leaf-like fossil insects in the Upper Jurassic, when deciduous trees had not yet evolved. According to this argument, leaf-like anatomical structures can evolve only when leaves are present. This would imply that the leaves must have had some mysterious influence on the genetic mutations of the animals. It is far more reasonable, surely, to assume that characters resembling some object or other repeatedly arise by chance mutation, even if the model is somewhere else. If both characters happen to coincide temporally and spatially with a signal-receiver which may compare the two, then the signal-receiver may exert a selective pressure. This pressure may result only in the retention of the imitation and it need not necessarily spread through conspecifies in a population and need not undergo a process of perfection. Let us assume that a certain grasshopper, which for some reason has a leaf-like appearance, is living in an area where no leaves of similar form occur. If leaf-bearing plants then appeared in the area and the grasshopper suffered less predation because it was more difficult to find than before, are we not entitled to employ the terms mimicry and mimetic patterns? Those who disagree with this must provide proof in all cases of mimicry that the model is more ancient than the mimetic effect.

It may be that some prefer to accept this restricted definition, but this has little to do with the question whether a similarity between two different objects deceives some other organism. Nor does it concern the effect of the illusion on the organisms concerned. These two questions strike me as being the central questions in mimicry at present. Finally, the necessary triangular relationship in mimicry of model, mimic and signal-receiver need not necessarily arise by the introduction of a mimic to the dual model-signal-receiver system. If it is assumed that a third agent must be attached to a dual system, then the added agent could be any of the three, model, mimic or signal-receiver, and it is pointless to define mimicry on the basis of any one of these.

12 Mertensian mimicry

Because of their extremely conspicuous coloration, a number of snakes found in the New World have earned the title coral snakes or coral vipers. At the time when Henry Bates announced his idea of mimicry in South American butterflies, it was already known that some of the coral snakes were poisonous and that others were harmless. In fact, one speaks of true and false coral snakes, implicitly accepting that the conspicuous colour pattern represents a scaring or warning device in the case of the dangerous snakes. This has naturally given rise to the notion that the false coral snakes are examples of mimicry – an interpretation that soon came under heavy discussion. A number of herpetologists rejected the idea of mimicry in coral snakes, while others produced a number of arguments in favour of mimicry, in some cases with great treatment and often rather clumsily. In 1956, Professor Mertens, a prominent herpetologist, discussed the problem in detail. His account is of particular interest, since he was originally sceptical, if not positively opposed to mimicry as applied to coral snakes, and he switched over to become a supporter of the theory when he examined the facts in the field.

When coral snakes glide along rapidly they all look very similar. A specialist in 1927, however, described the harmless *Atractus latifrons* as a new species of *Micrurus*, so some species may even be confused when lying still for examination. The various patterns to be found in these snakes can often be distinguished only when several coral snakes are examined simultaneously. Mertens distinguishes the following types on the basis of the number of adjacent black rings in each group in the pattern. The yellow can be very light, sometimes even white:

1. Red-yellow-black-yellow-red;
   black bands occur singly.
2. Red-black-yellow-black-red;
   black bands occurring in groups of two.
3. Red-black-yellow-black-yellow-black-red;
   black bands occurring in groups of three.

4. Red-black-yellow-black-yellow-black-yellow-black-red; black bands occurring in groups of four.
5. It is possible that the yellow areas between the black bands of type 3 may contain black stripes of varying degrees of development.
   This gives a total of 5 bands, three broad and two narrow, in each group.

It must be mentioned, however, that this classification sometimes makes the similarities appear greater than they actually are. The differently coloured rings can vary in width and this alters the appearance of the animal considerably, as is shown in the segments in figure 23.

The coral pattern can be found in about seventy-five species of snake belonging to eighteen genera, all living in the tropical or subtropical zone of the New World. Coral snakes belong to two separate families, the poisonous Elapidae and the non-poisonous Colubridae. It is easier to summarise the relationships between kinship, poisonousness, and coloration when these are considered two at a time.

Poisonousness and kinship The fangs, originally developed for holding prey, may be completely smooth, in which case they are called aglyph. Snakes possessing smooth fangs are non-poisonous. On the other hand, the fangs may possess a groove that connects with the outlet of a poison gland. If the hind teeth in the upper jaw are grooved, they are called opisthoglyph. Snakes with grooved hind teeth are weakly to moderately poisonous. Snakes with grooved fangs (the teeth at the front of the upper jaw) are termed proteroglyph and can be moderately to dangerously poisonous. (The vipers have the most specialised tooth-form, which possess a longitudinal canal that functions as a poison syringe. This condition is called solenoglyph.)

Poisonous snakes have progressively specialised the poison for killing prey. But here we are concerned with the defensive be-

Figure 23. 'Coral snakes' is a collective term given to a number of neotropical snakes because of their conspicuous coloration. The colour patterns are to a great extent based upon similar colour combinations, but the similarities do not result from any relationship between the species. The segments shown clarify the patterns mentioned in the text. Top: *Lampropeltis doliata annulata*. Middle: *Micrurus fulvius*. Bottom: *Micruroides euryxanthus*.

haviour of the snake in response to enemies which threaten it. Our question is: how does the snake defend itself? The most poisonous of the coral snakes are the cobra relatives, and these can quickly kill a small mammal or bird. These snakes are not very prone to bite in defence, and even *Pseudoboa trigemina* does not bite very readily. On the other hand, the small *Erythrolamprus aesculapii venustissimus*, a moderately poisonous snake, is extremely vicious. Thus there are various degrees of viciousness and poisonousness, and these two factors together constitute danger.

The danger attached to these snakes bears no relationship to the family tree. The same sub-family may contain poisonous and non-poisonous snakes. There are even aglyphic forms within the genus *Erythrolamprus*, which also contains poisonous forms, some of which are described here.

Coloration and kinship The coral pattern is only found in New World snakes of the Elaphidae and the Colubridae, but not all snakes of this region exhibit this pattern. The genus *Micrurus*, which belongs to the true coral snakes, contains one species, *M. bipartitus*, which does not have the coral pattern, and is simply ringed in black and white. In South America, the genus *Sibynophis* exhibits all stages leading to the full coral pattern: the pattern is completely lacking in *S.sumichrasti; S.carpicinctus* bears black and yellow alternating stripes on its neck, and these spread on to the neck and anterior back in *S.annulatus*, and spread farther in *S.nothus* to include everything except the tail, and finally cover the entire dorsal aspect in *S.cyclurus*. In this series, red gradually appears and eventually becomes the ground-colour.

Similarity in colour is therefore no indication of kinship and is not determined by ancestry. Conversely, difference in coloration is no argument against relationship, and this applies particularly to the differentiation of the coloration types.

Poisonousness and coloration It was mentioned at the very beginning that these two factors are not correlated. There are poisonous and non-poisonous species which look alike. But it cannot be taken as a general rule that two species with the same markings represent one poisonous and one non-poisonous form. Both may be poisonous or non-poisonous, and they need not necessarily be related. More than two species may also exhibit the same colour pattern, in which case one or more may be poisonous.

If the coloration of coral snakes is related neither to kinship nor to poisonousness, what does it depend upon? We cannot assume that such colour patterns occur by chance only in South America. There can be no correlation with environment, since coral snakes occur in rain forests, in bushy steppes, in mountain areas, and in dry, desert-like regions. In any case, related snakes occur in corresponding regions in other parts of the world without developing coral patterning. There is also no relationship to the diet of the animals; many coral snakes, but not all, are snake-eaters, but snake-eating serpents in the Old World look entirely different. Perhaps something mysterious and peculiar to South America is responsible for the coral pattern, but why does this something only affect snakes about one metre in length, and not larger snakes or those only forty centimetres long? The coral pattern is very conspicuous in all the environments mentioned, and so there is no question of camouflage. In addition, the majority are not nocturnal and do not conceal themselves like other snakes. *Pseudoboa* and *Rhinobothryum* are exceptions in that they are active at night, thus showing that coloration is also independent of the time of day. We have to look somewhere else for an explanation of coloration in coral snakes.

After extensive evaluation of all the arguments, Mertens comes to the conclusion that the originally suggested interpretation, that of mimicry, is the likeliest explanation. We must then assume that the ubiquitous light-dark annulation of the New World poisonous vipers once gave rise to the black-yellow(white)-red coral patterning. The pattern is of advantage to poisonous species as a warning effect, since at least some of the snake's enemies are deterred. It should then be possible for a harmless snake to enjoy the same protection just by displaying the same coloration. Similar colour patterns occur again and again, while many snake species are extremely variable in their markings. Even some harmless snakes in areas other than America show traces of the coral pattern, although in these cases they are very conspicuous and are thus liable to attack since the protective effect of the models is lacking.

An attempt to produce a neat explanation of all coral patterns is doomed to failure. The only satisfactory explanation so far produced gives different reasons for poisonous and non-poisonous forms, and assumes that the poisonous forms are a necessary prerequisite to the existence of non-poisonous forms. The fact that so many different snakes with the coral pattern are to be found concentrated in South America is quite simply dependent upon the restriction of the few poisonous coral vipers to this area. This also explains a number of other remarkable features. As has been mentioned, the coral pattern is lacking in snakes which are bigger than the poisonous coral snakes. This agreement with the model is particularly obvious in the case of *Lampropeltis doliata gaigae*, where the coral pattern is restricted to a particular phase in the life-cycle. Juvenile animals of this subspecies resemble members of the genus *Micrurus*, whereas the adult snake, which is much bigger, is completely black. Further, *Lampropeltis doliata* in the north east of the United States has no coral pattern; the pattern is restricted to the south, in those areas where *Micrurus* occurs.

Signal-receiver and model The reader will already have noticed that the similarity of *Micrurus* species to one another falls under the heading of Müllerian mimicry and not Batesian mimicry. But it is difficult to classify *Rhinobothryum*, *Erythrolamprus* and *Pseudoboa*, which are indeed poisonous and yet not as poisonous as *Micrurus*. To the extent that they are themselves protected, they represent Müllerian mimics, but the fact that this protection is lesser in extent would classify them as Batesian mimics. This is not so tragic, though, since we have already seen that there are stages of gradation between these two types of mimicry. The whole problem becomes complicated, however, as soon as the signal-receivers are taken into account because the conclusion is then reached that it is not the *Micrurus* species but their less poisonous 'mimics' which are the actual models, that is, the protective agency. It is essential to realise, first of all, that snakes have a whole range of enemies. In South America, the most important are small carnivores, which are heavily dependent upon snakes for food; then come cuckoos,

Figure 24. The poisonous coral snake *Micrurus frontalis* and the non-poisonous *Simophis rhinostoma* can scarcely be distinguished unless they are examined side by side. In this case the poisonous form is not the model for the non-poisonous form: both are mimics.

storks, the seriemas (Cariamidae), roughly corresponding to the African secretary-birds (Sagitariidae), and other animals such as large, snake-eating vipers, for example, the Mussurana (*Clelia*). Some of these animals even cope with the most poisonous snakes. No animal species, of course, has absolute protection. Nevertheless, a relative degree of protection which slightly reduces the number of predators is of great advantage. There is no evidence that these snake predators can recognise a true coral snake innately, that is, without prior experience. But it has already been mentioned that the venom of the true coral snakes is extremely poisonous if an animal is bitten; a mouse will drop dead on the spot if bitten by *Micrurus corallinus* or *M.fulvius*. Even when the fatal effect is somewhat slower, one is forced to ask what function the conspicuous coral pattern might have. These snakes could, in fact, have any other patterning, particularly one with a cryptic effect, since all such snakes have enemies which learn nothing from the unpleasant effects of an unsuccessful attack; the attacker does not have another opportunity to encounter a situation where it might recognise a dangerous adversary. This being the case, the conspicuous coral pattern of the true coral snakes cannot be a warning pattern, since each predator would then have to learn the warning by trial and error, and the first error costs the predator its life. On the other hand, this warning pattern can be learnt from experience with similarly coloured false coral snakes producing mild poison because the bitten animal can recover. Such a victim would then naturally keep out of the way of the identically coloured true coral snakes. The protective function of the coral pattern in the true coral snakes is thus dependent on unpleasant experiences which predators encounter with moderately poisonous, false coral snakes. At the other extreme, the completely harmless false coral snakes are equally dependent upon the intermediate forms. We therefore reach the conclusion that the moderately poisonous species are the true protective agents (the models) and that both the non-poisonous and the fatally poisonous species are to be regarded as mimics.

It is obvious that the non-poisonous, inoffensive forms are mimics in Bates' sense; but the fatally poisonous forms are not Batesian mimics, since they are protected, probably to a greater extent than the models. An animal which has encountered unpleasant experiences with the moderately poisonous species will indeed avoid the fatally poisonous species, but with good reason, as typical of Müllerian mimicry, and not unneccessarily, as is typical of Batesian mimicry. In fact, the predator's life is saved because it underestimates the fatally poisonous mimic. Nevertheless, it is not possible to speak of Müllerian mimicry, since the protective function of the warning pattern is not a mutual effect. The moderately poisonous species does not have the warning pattern because it is possessed by the fatally poisonous types; the effect is one-way.

This form of mimicry, where the most offensive species is not the model because it is *too* offensive to allow the signal-receiver to learn and is instead the mimic of a less offensive species, could perhaps be called *Mertensian mimicry*. This type of mimicry should theoretically be expected to occur among very offensive and poisonous animals of other groups, perhaps among spined insects, which can be dangerous for small predators. Until now, there has only been one explanation for the presence of warning coloration in animals which kill their enemies: it has been postulated that the pattern is innately recognised. Mertensian mimicry provides an alternative explanation in that the warning coloration, as in the case of Batesian and Müllerian mimicry, need be regarded only as a particularly effective training device.

One would also speak of Mertensian mimicry where the threatened animal does not kill its enemy but only eliminates the sense organ necessary for the recognition of a similar prey.For example, it would be sufficient for a snake with warning coloration to defend itself by spraying poison in the eyes of the attacker and blinding it.

Mertens did not himself draw this conclusion from his studies of coral snakes. He attempts to classify everything as Batesian or Müllerian mimicry. In addition, he lays great value on Wallace's frequency criterion, according to which mimics cannot be more common than models. We have already seen that this is not necessarily correct. The numbers quoted by Mertens are nevertheless of interest. Trappers continually bring snakes of all species to the famous Butantan Institut in Sao Paulo, totalling 14,000 to 26,000 snakes per year. Most important, the trappers do not distinguish true and false 'cobras corales' and are not encouraged to do so. The frequency with which the individual species arrive thus corresponds to the frequency with which the trappers encounter them. The following data were obtained for the Sao Paulo area:

	1950	1951	1952	1953
Models	59	41	58	56
Mimics	218	246	265	284

If the frequency criterion is accepted, these data speak against mimicry, since the mimics represent over 80 per cent of the catches. The values for the whole of Brazil are 65 per cent to 75 per cent. In addition, there are areas in the south west of the United States where coral snakes occur in the absence of the *Micrurus* forms as models.

But this presentation of the data is built on the general assumption that the *Micrurus* species act as models and that all other forms are mimics. But, as we have seen, this assumption is probably erroneous. If the data presented above are re-arranged, taking the moderately poisonous species (*Erythrolamprus*, *Pseudoboa*) as models and both the non-poisonous (*Simphis rhinostoma*) and fatally poisonous forms (*Micrurus* species) as mimics, the following table is obtained:

	1950	1951	1952	1953
Models	193	220	236	257
Mimics	84	67	87	83

The proportions have been roughly reversed, and there are actually more models than mimics.

Mertens explains the evolution of mimicry among the coral snakes with a two-step theory built on a strong foundation. The Elapidae must have reached the New World by migration across the North Pacific land-bridge from the Old World, at the latest during the Late Mesozoic or the Early Tertiary. Thus, mimicry in the coral snakes may be older than sixty million years. The true coral snakes were presumably less poisonous at the beginning of their evolution, that is, from an ancestor of *Micrurus*. As moderately poisonous species, they could have played the role of model, so that the evolution of identical warning coloration was advantageous for very poisonous or non-poisonous species. As mentioned before, the genus *Erythrolamprus* contains both opisthoglyphic and aglyphic forms. This is a convincing indication that poisonous qualities have gradually increased during the evolution of these snakes. If this is true, the present-day (second) step in the evolution of coral snake mimicry must have arisen inevitably. The original models probably became too poisonous to carry out their former role, whereas a proportion of the original mimics gradually evolved to become models. Whether or not this is true, the coral snakes very clearly demonstrate how important it is to know the reactions, or possible reactions, of the signal-receiver in order to evaluate the roles of model and mimic with any degree of accuracy.

13 Aggressive mimicry involving three or more species

An old metaphor, dating back to the Bible, is that of the wolf in sheep's clothing. Primitive peoples often use a disguise when hunting and camouflage themselves as harmless animals. The most common ploy is to adopt the guise of the animal species which is being hunted. Australian aborigines, for example, disguise themselves as kangaroos when hunting and copy their jumping mode of locomotion. They make mock pauses, pretending to groom themselves or to graze, and so on. In brief, the hunters imitate the prey in order to deceive the hunted.

There is also the well-known nursery tale about the wolf and the seven baby goats. The baby goats, whose mother is away, know that strangers can be dangerous and intend to open the door to nobody else. The wolf asks to be let in, pretending to be their mother returning from an excursion. But the baby goats recognise him because his voice is too deep. The wolf then goes off to a shopkeeper, buys some chalk and eats it in order to mellow his voice. He then tries his luck again. The baby goats are careful, however, and they ask to see a part of his body. The wolf rests his paws against the windowpane, and the baby goats, seeing that his paws are not white, still refuse to let him in. The wolf then goes to the baker and spreads sticky dough on his paws, following this with a visit to the miller who is told to strew white flour on the dough. Thus prepared, the wolf makes his third visit to the baby goats. Since the necessary details are all in order on this visit, the baby goats let the wolf in and he gobbles them up, except for one, who is left to tell mother everything and ensure a happy ending. In this story it was enough that the main features employed in recognition were visible.

The cobler Wilhelm Voigt became famous following a stunt which he pulled off in Berlin-Köpenick on the 16 October, 1906. Voigt donned a stolen army captain's uniform, stopped a number of soldiers on the street, took them with him into the town hall, confiscated the contents of the city treasury and arrested the mayor. To pull off this stunt he made good use of the fact that the reactions of his fellow citizens were largely dependent upon a restricted number of sign stimuli, so that any person bearing an

appropriately coloured uniform would be treated as a captain.
These examples, of course, do not come under the heading of Batesian mimicry, since all the mimics so far mentioned want something from the model, or at least do something under the protection of the model. In Batesian mimicry, however, the mimic simply requires to be left in peace. Many examples can be found in the animal kingdom. One, provided by Willis, is the rare zone-tailed hawk (*Buteo albonotatus*), which glides in the company of a group of vultures in America. This is the only American buzzard species which is nearly black, and whose wings are long and narrow like those of a vulture. The zone-tailed hawk does not use a look-out perch, and does not hover – it glides. Now vultures present no threat to small animals and therefore do not instil fear in them. The buzzard exploits this and suddenly dives from the vulture group and takes its prey by surprise. This is referred to as *aggressive mimicry*. The concept was introduced by E. G. Peckham, and an extension of the usual habit of using the author's name in classifying mimicry would justify using the term *Peckhammian mimicry*. This type of mimicry roughly corresponds to the camouflage adopted by spies, who play the part of harmless members of the society which they intend to damage. (An analogy of Batesian mimicry is provided by attempts made by certain spies during the war to remain unmolested under the protection of the Red Cross, while not actually performing Red Cross duties). In aggressive mimicry, the predator is thus identical with the mimic. The first examples of this type of mimicry were once again derived from insects. It was assumed that some hover-flies very similar in appearance to bees or bumble-bees sneaked into bees' nests under protection of their overall resemblance and then desposited their parasitic larvae. It is not yet known whether this interpretation is correct. Other examples of aggressive mimicry have been investigated in detail and provide some of the best documented illustrations of mimetic effects.

Anglers

In angling, one can catch fish either by dangling a hook masked with a food morsel, such as a worm, so that the fish swallows the hook in taking the prey, or by the use of a lure consisting of nothing more than a piece of metal. Such non-edible lures can be used to catch predatory fish such as pike. But why is a pike fooled by the lure? It has often been mentioned that many fish swimming in open water are extremely well camouflaged by virtue of their coloration: they have dark backs and silvery bellies. Diseased or injured fish do not swim in the proper manner and wobble easily, which makes them flash under water. An irregular flashing stimulus thus acts as a signal for the predatory fish to bite. The lure of the angler provides exactly this signal and the pike bites into the hook. Salmon can be similarly trapped with a 'fly', which imitates an insect dancing on the surface of the water.

The term angler is not only applied to the sportsman; it is also the name of a group of fish known as the Lophiiformes. These fish do not angle as a pastime, but live by it, as was known to Aristotle. The European coastline bordering the Atlantic is inhabited by the sea devil (*Lophius piscatorius*). Specimens up to one-and-a-half metres long are sometimes captured and the pancreas is used to provide insulin. The fish lives on the bottom and has a markedly flattened belly. The dorsal fin is peculiar in that the anterior fin-rays are not joined with skin. The foremost ray is located on a ball-joint set on the dorsal edge of the upper lip some distance in front of the eyes. This ray (the illicium) bears a fleshy cutaneous appendage on its tip (the esca, or bait) which is held in front of the mouth and swung in all directions. If another fish snaps at this dummy prey, the angler swallows the attacker.

Smaller, related species are very common in tropical waters. The appendage on the first dorsal fin-ray varies greatly in appearance, though all anglers employ it as a lure. The lure of *Phrynelox* has the appearance of a pink worm and can actively coil and uncoil, while the fin-ray, which is practically transparent, can be jerked in all directions. The angler-fish are quite enterprising creatures. They often resemble stones overgrown with bryozoans and sometimes bear a coat of cutaneous outgrowths which look like encrustations of lamellar algae. These fish do not possess powerful teeth, to enable them to take a tight grip on the prey. Instead, they wait motionless until a fish becomes interested in the lure. The lure is then vibrated in different directions in front of the mouth with great vigour. When the prey is about to snap at the lure, the angler swallows violently and sucks the prey and the surrounding water into its stomach. The entire mouth and gill chamber is adapted for this manner of eating. The gill-slits have been reduced on both sides, leaving no more than two small round apertures to ensure that water cannot flow in the wrong direction. Since the fish victim always swims towards the lure head-first, it is taken into the jaws from this position. It can be demonstrated experimentally that the angler has great difficulty in holding and swallowing its prey 'against the grain'.

These angler species, which are usually less than 30 cm in length, bear lures of extremely varied form on the angling fin-ray, and some lures resemble bundles of algae. In some cases, it is obvious that the dummy bait is intended for a particular prey species. For example, the species with the dummy worm mentioned above (*Phrynelox*) only catches worm-eating fish. The bizarre bat-fish (genus *Ogcocephalus*) angles downwards to catch small crustaceans on the sandy substrate, using a specially constructed angling rod. The angling ray grows out from the forehead between the eyes and is covered by a dorsal bony extension of the skull. Deep-sea anglers of the family Ceratiidae have luminous lures in various colours, sometimes suspended from extremely long 'fishing rods'. Of course, little is known about these deep-sea forms, but there is plenty of opportunity to carry out observations on other angler-fish living at easily accessible depths.

Angling is a very comfortable way of obtaining food, and this technique is not confined to fish. The alligator snapping-turtle *Macroclemmys temmincki*, a native of the Mississippi area, also uses

Figure 25. Four examples of predators that angle for their prey with dummy bait. Top left: the angling turtle *Macroclemmys temmincki.* Bottom left: the catfish *Chaca chaca.* Top right: the angler-fish *Phrynelox scaber*. Bottom right: the closely related bat-fish *Ogcocephalus*, which angles for small crustaceans living on the substrate, and therefore directs its lure downwards.

this method of predation. The triple-keeled shell of this huge reptile, which may reach two hundred pounds in weight, is covered with a thick layer of encrusting algae, which provides admirable camouflage. In addition, the turtle remains partly buried and immobile in the mud, apart from occasional vital trips to the surface to breathe. A hungry alligator snapping-turtle opens its mouth wide. Both the lining of the mouth and the thick tongue are darkly pigmented, whereas the tip of the tongue bears a two-pronged appendage covered with red spots. The appendage is twitched around by muscular contractions. Fish which are searching for prey that resemble such an appendage gradually approach this mobile structure and try to snap at it. To do this, however, they have to extend their fore-quarters into the wide-open mouth of the turtle. The powerful, hook-shaped jaws snap together in a flash. This sequence of events can easily be observed in an aquarium. It is then seen, as in the case of the angler-fish, that only worm-eating fish fall prey to these predators.

It has been reported that some of the huge and pugnacious South American horned frogs (genus *Ceratophrys*) will sit still and move one finger of the hand. This is supposed to arouse the attention of other animals, even smaller frogs. These other animals attempt to capture the apparent prey and end up inside the stomach of *Ceratophrys*. I am not sure whether these cases are chance happenings or regular occurrences. It should nevertheless be borne in mind that most small animals spend the greater part of their time in search of food and can be attracted to dummy prey with a fair degree of certainty. This is not to say that all attractive features possessed by the mimic are developed for this sole purpose. We spread jam on our bread for a purpose other than that of attracting wasps, but they sometimes turn up just the same.

The large forest areas of West, Central and East Africa are inhabited by the potto *Perodicticus potto*, a loris scarcely the size of a cat. This animal climbs around in the dark on the branches of trees and searches for insects, various fruits and, according to reports, birds. Occasionally, the potto exudes a strong odour, which possibly originates from a glandular area on the scrotum in males and the edges of the vulva in females, which produce a sebaceous secretion. It is not known whether the potto marks its territory with this substance as other lorises do or whether this plays a part in sexual behaviour, but this can reasonably be assumed from what is known of other loris species. What is certain is that the glandular secretion has a remarkable side-effect. Various insects, roaches, bluebottles, flies and wax-moths, persistently attempt to reach the source of the odour and will even leave bright light to enter a dark cage occupied by a potto. Cowgill wiped a ball of cotton-wool over the glandular area of a potto and subsequently attracted insects with the treated cotton-wool. A potto in captivity can easily obtain prize wax-moths in this way.

Minor improvements in extremely crude prey dummies are particularly rewarding for those animals that exploit the appetite of their prey in order to satisfy their own. The marine snail *Vermetus* (a member of the Prosobranchia) possesses a firmly-anchored shell which juts upwards from the substrate as a series of irregular arches. The snail peers upwards from the entrance to this shell, and in response to certain stimuli from micro-organisms, or acting on suspicion of such, it extrudes a mucous band from its foot. Terrestrial snails use this mucous secretion to aid in their creeping mode of locomotion, but *Vermetus* is firmly fixed to the substrate, and the mucous strand floats free in the water. After a while, the strand is retrieved, the free end is taken up and the strand is ingested together with the attached planktonic organisms. The snail thus fishes like a fisherman with the slime net. An expanded fishing net, however, can be made attractive, and more efficient, by the application of extra stimuli. Many fishermen switch on lamps at night as a means of attracting photo-sensitive fish. Some fungus gnats in New Zealand have larvae which exploit the fact that insects are particularly attracted towards a light. These larvae are solitary occupants of caves, crevices and holes in steep river banks. They construct a horizontal supporting thread from which a large number of trap-threads covered with sticky droplets are

Figure 26. The larva of the New Zealand fungus gnat *Bolitophila luminosa* rests on a horizontal thread from which are suspended trap-threads with sticky droplets. The larva illuminates this curtain with its luminescent organ and eats insects which adhere to the threads.

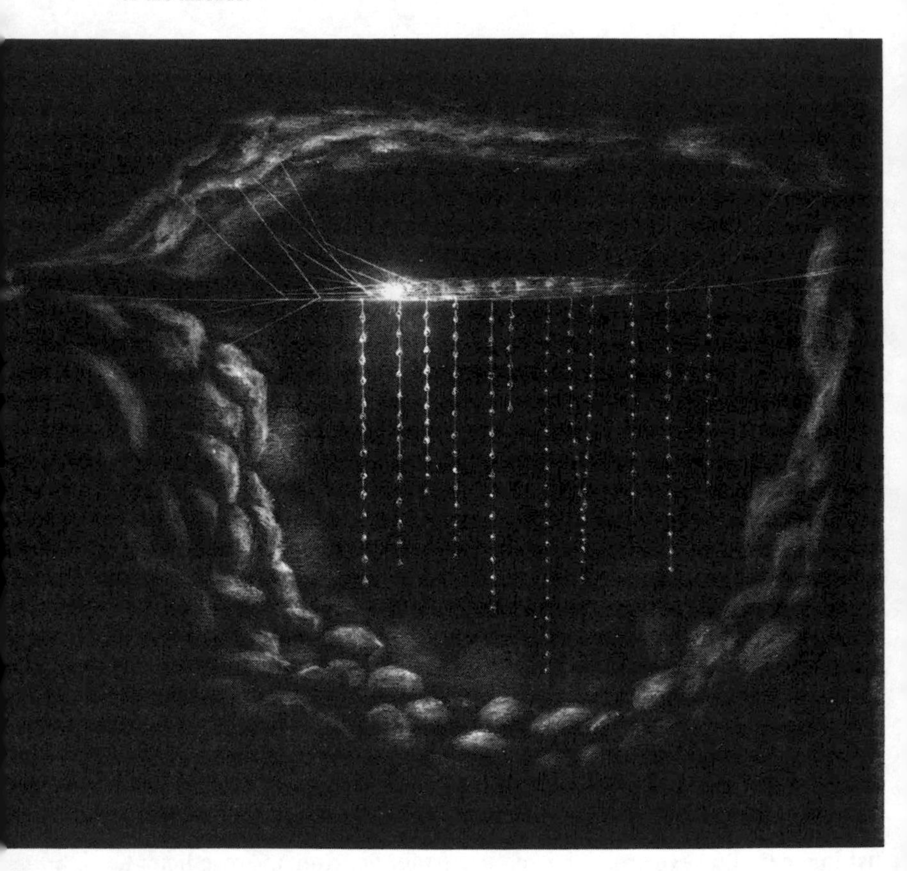

suspended to depths ranging from three to fifty centimetres. The larva is itself no more than three centimetres long and carries a luminous organ at its tail end. This organ is formed from the Malpighian bodies, which serve for the excretion of metabolic waste, and its ventral half is covered by a bowl-shaped reflector. When darkness falls, the larva lies along the supporting thread

Figure 27. Bola spiders (here the American species *Mastophora*) do not build an orb-web. Instead, they hold a trap-thread with a terminal sticky droplet 'in one hand' and either twirl it in a circle or aim it at fairly large insects which happen to fly past.

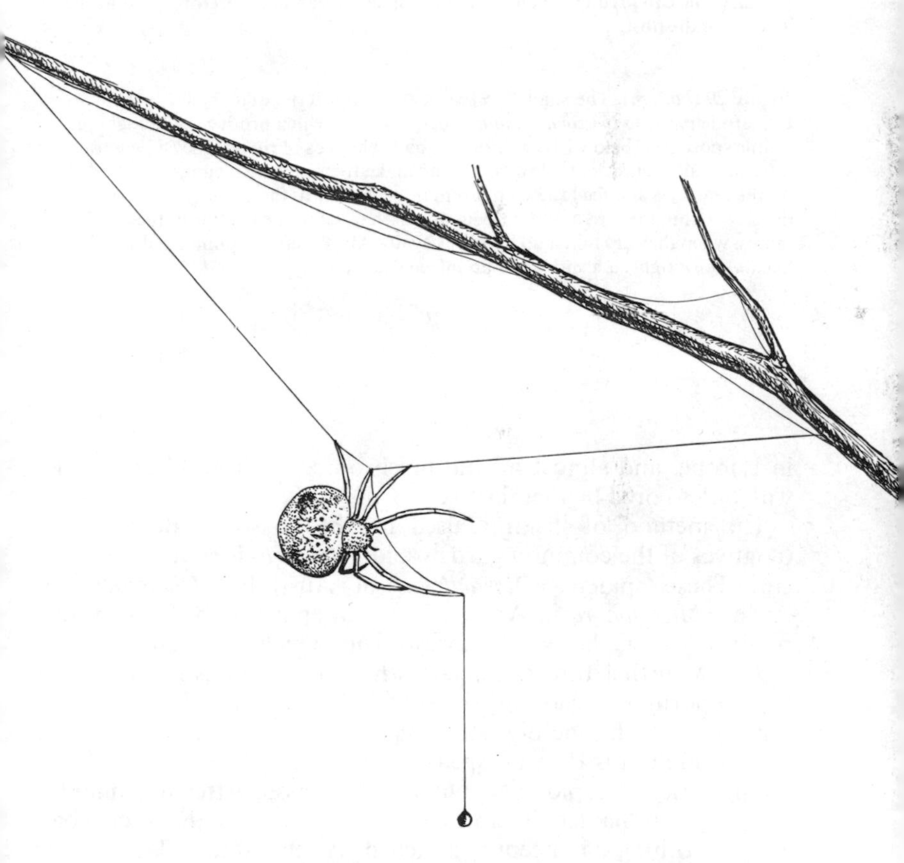

with its stomach pointing upwards and illuminates the pearly threads below. If an insect flies into the trap, the larva climbs down and eats the prey. The trap-thread is then repaired and the larva returns to keep watch. During the day, or in response to a disturbance at night, the larva creeps into a retreat at one end of the supporting thread. Fungus gnats incidentally, are also found

Figure 28 (*top*). The giant cercaria *Cercaria mirabilis* is a larval form of a trematode. The cercaria's appearance and its hopping mode of locomotion (some phases of which are shown, arrows indicating sequence of phases and direction of movement), cause it to resemble a swimming, small crustacean or mosquito larva with the result that fish swallow the parasite, mistaking it for food. Research on these parasites is made much easier when one recognises that these larval stages often mimic the food-organisms of their respective hosts. In fact, by observing the parasite, one can predict which animal it is likely to eat and therefore guess at the identity of the host.

Figure 29 (*bottom*). The snail *Succinea* acts as an intermediate host for the trematode parasite *Leucochloridium macrostomum*, which produces a branching, motile sporocyst (below left) within the snail. The sacs of the sporocyst penetrate into the snail's tentacles (below right) and make them so conspicuous that birds bite off the tentacles and feed these apparent insect larvae to their young. The parasites develop within the bird and their eggs are discharged to the outside in the host's faeces, when they are taken up by snails again. Above left: an uninfected snail's head. Above right: a healthy and an infected snail.

in Europe, and almost all old mushrooms in the wild are riddled with holes bored by their larvae.

The method of 'fishing' used by the Lasso or Bola Spiders (relatives of the common garden spider *Aranea*) is somewhat different. These spiders (*Dicrostichus* in Australia. *Cladomelea* in Africa, *Mastophora* in America) do not spin a web. Instead, they produce a single horizontal thread from which they suspend themselves. A further thread coated with sticky droplets is attached to the supporting thread and the spider then brushes all the droplets together to form one big, sticky ball at the free end of the thread. This pendulum is then grasped with one leg. *Cladomelea* performs a long series of rapid rotations with the lasso. After five minutes, the thread is hauled in and eaten together with the sticky ball, even if nothing has become attached. A few minutes later, a new lasso is prepared and 'fishing' is continued. *Dicrostichus* employs roughly the same method, but does not swing the lasso around until an insect actually approaches. In contrast, *Mastophora* does not swing its lasso round in a circle, but aims it at approaching insects. If no insect approaches within half an hour, this species will also eat the lasso and then make a new one.

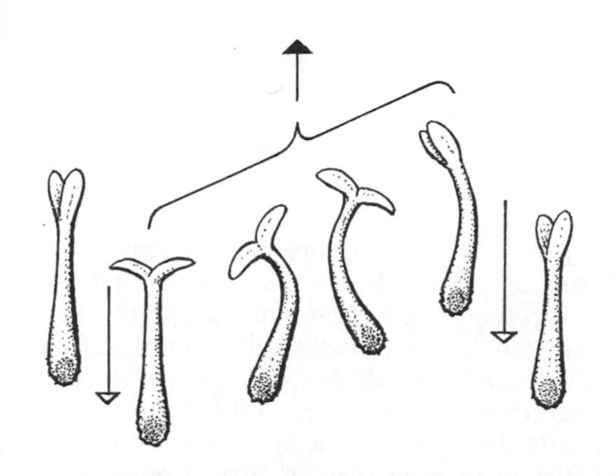

At first sight, these methods of catching prey would appear to have little chance of success. Nevertheless, the Lasso Spiders obviously catch enough for their needs, and since they are nocturnal, they catch mainly small, nocturnally active moths. But this is not the whole story. Almost all observers were at first amazed at the strike accuracy of these spiders, until they noticed that the moths flew towards the spider or the lasso ball with conspicuous regularity. Moths were even seen to turn around and offer themselves again if the spider did not strike home the first time. Many observations have fortified the suspicion that the spider must use some form of attractant, possibly an olfactory stimulus. It is not known whether this is a food stimulus or a sexual attractant, since nobody has investigated this phenomenon. Added speculation has little point, but later on we shall see actual examples of the misuse and exploitation of specific olfactory stimuli.

Trematodes

The Trematodes are a group of parasitic worms belonging to the phylum Platyhelminthes. One parasite, *Leucochloridium macrostomum*, resides principally in the intestine of song-birds. The eggs of the parasite pass to the outside in the bird's faeces, which are readily ingested by the well-known terrestrial snail *Succinea*, an inhabitant of water-logged meadows and banks alongside bodies of water. The eggs hatch into various larval forms within the snail, and one of these stages, called the sporocyst, is strikingly green in colour and bears yellow-brown rings. A sporocyst-sac then presses into each of the two tentacles of the snail and begins to pulsate violently at roughly 40 to 70 beats per minute. The tentacle of the snail becomes greatly enlarged by its burden and eventually forms a transparent covering over the pulsating sporocyst. *Succinea* usually avoids light, but infected specimens do not. This is all that is necessary for a song-bird to mistake the conspicuous tentacle for an insect larva, bite it off, and eat it. From the sporocyst then hatch the final larvae which grow into adult worms inside the bird. The snail's tentacle soon regenerates and the story is repeated when another sporocyst-sac passes into a new tentacle. The sporocysts of other Trematodes are neither brightly coloured nor mobile. Colour and pulsation are necessary to *Leucochlorodium*, however, for arousing the interest of insectivorous birds. The host birds do not eat snails, so the sporocyst has to imitate the bird's food.

We have already seen that some animals camouflage themselves in order to make themselves less conspicuous, while others adopt warning coloration to prevent themselves from being eaten, whether or not they are really inedible. In contrast, the sporocyst of *Leucochloridium* makes itself conspicuous so that it *is* eaten. This is perfectly appropriate for an endoparasite, and really represents an unusual case of aggressive mimicry.

Fish and shellfish

The rivers of North America are inhabited by species of shellfish related to the European swan-mussels (Unionidae). The fertilised eggs of the shellfish are transferred to a special area of the gill-chamber called the marsupium, where the eggs develop into larvae called glochidia. These later escape from the marsupium and as many as 300,000 glochidia are liberated in one burst. In one genus, *Lampsilis*, the glochidia have to clamp on to the gills of a fish, where they digest the superficial layer of gill tissue, possibly including the blood of the gills in their diet. After a time, the larvae develop into the adult mollusc and then fall off the fish.

Now it is known that the glochidia cannot reach the gills unaided – they must be actively taken up by the fish. Some *Lampsilis* species live in rivers and streams with fast-flowing water where the substrate is sandy. Here, the larvae cannot lie on the substrate and wait until they are scooped up, which is possible with *Lampsilis* species living on the mud of lakes. Some *Lampsilis* species have found instead a most elegant way of reaching the host. A female *Lampsilis* develops an outgrowth on the mantle margin when carrying larvae. The outgrowth is shaped like a papilla, lobe, flap or ribbon, and lies near the exhalent aperture of the shellfish. In *Lampsilis nasuta*, a white point moves conspicuously up and down in a gap between the two mantle margins. The mantle margin of *L.radiata* produces a bifid appendage which performs twitching movements, which could be compared to those of a fish's tail. In all probability, these movements attract the attention of fish, which approach in order to examine the potential prey at close quarters. This could be an advantage to the shellfish since it would then have a prospective host at which to let fly its glochidia at short range.

Although these suppositions have not been confirmed by experiment, it has been possible to obtain a number of further details from personal communications with Dr Haas and Dr Welsh. The mantle appendage of *L.fasciola* closely resembles a fish, and that of *L.ovata ventricosa* is amazingly fish-like. The appendage of the latter species bears an anterior 'head' with an eye-spot and a posterior 'fish tail', the terms anterior and posterior being in contrast to the mussel's anatomy. The black eye-spot is also found in the male, although little developed, and the remainder of the outgrowth is considerably smaller. As long as the female mussel remains undisturbed, the edges of the valves are kept slightly apart and the marsupium containing the larvae is extended upwards so that it projects slightly above the valves. The outgrowths of the mantle margin lie with their lobed edges dangling free in the water. The lobes undulate rhythmically with waves passing from the eye-spot to the 'tail' (anatomically, from posterior to anterior). A water current is thus directed over the protruding edge of the marsupium. The entire movement was probably originally developed for aeration of the brooding gills, but an additional function has been acquired. The shellfish sits with the anterior end pointing away from the current and the posterior edge of the valves facing the current. In this way, the paired mantle outgrowth 'swims' horizontally with the eye-spot directed against the current. Since the outgrowth is grey outside, and orange on the inside with a longitudinal black stripe, it stands out clearly against the white marsupium, which has a black edge. This gives a convincing impression

Figure 30. The larvae of many fresh-water snails begin life as ectoparasites of fish. The females of the North American clam *Lampsilis ovata ventricosa* bear a dummy fish formed from the edge of the mantle. When a predatory fish snaps at this apparent prey, the female clam blows its larvae into the fish's mouth.

of one or two small, moving fish. The movements stop in darkness or in direct sunlight, which means that the predominant function is no longer that of aeration of the larvae, since this would require a steady supply of oxygen. The movements also stop when the shellfish is briefly overshadowed, whether by an approaching fish or by a human hand held directly above. The shellfish then expels a ball of glochidia with such force that it is propelled some centimetres above the adult. It is very probable that this coincides with the position of the fish responsible for the shadow. The fish, attracted by the fish dummy on the female shellfish, receives a layer of parasitic shellfish larvae over its gills as thanks for its efforts.

Lampsilis is thus an example of both a parasite (as larvae) and an angler, although of course the adult shellfish does not devour the visiting fish or derive any direct benefit.

The praying mantis

One remarkable insect is the praying mantis (Mantidae), which is a rapacious relative of the grasshoppers. The insect owes its name to the posture of the powerful forelegs, for the shin (tibia) can be snapped back on to the thigh (femur). Both parts of the leg are covered with powerful spines for holding insect prey. Unlike typical grasshoppers, the mantis is carnivorous. It sits on plants and keeps a look-out for insects, which are trapped as soon as they fly within striking range of the forelegs. The mantis aims with amazing accuracy with the mobile head and thorax, and when the forelegs are extended, the victim has little chance of escaping. It takes only 50 to 55 milliseconds for the legs to extend and the pincers to snap around the prey; the reaction time of the prey lies between 50 and 80 milliseconds. When resting, the mantis holds it head and the elongated prothorax pointing upwards and the catching legs are held together as if in prayer. This sanctimonious posture has made these insects a source of superstition or even reverence for centuries, and the generic name *Mantis* means 'prophet'.

Most of the 1,800 or so known species of praying mantis are

Figure 31. Predatory insects of the family Mantidae have earned the title of 'praying mantis' because while waiting for prey they hold their grasping legs together, as in prayer. If an insect comes within range, the grasping legs shoot forwards and seize the prey. In the threat posture (bottom), the mantids spread out the grasping legs.

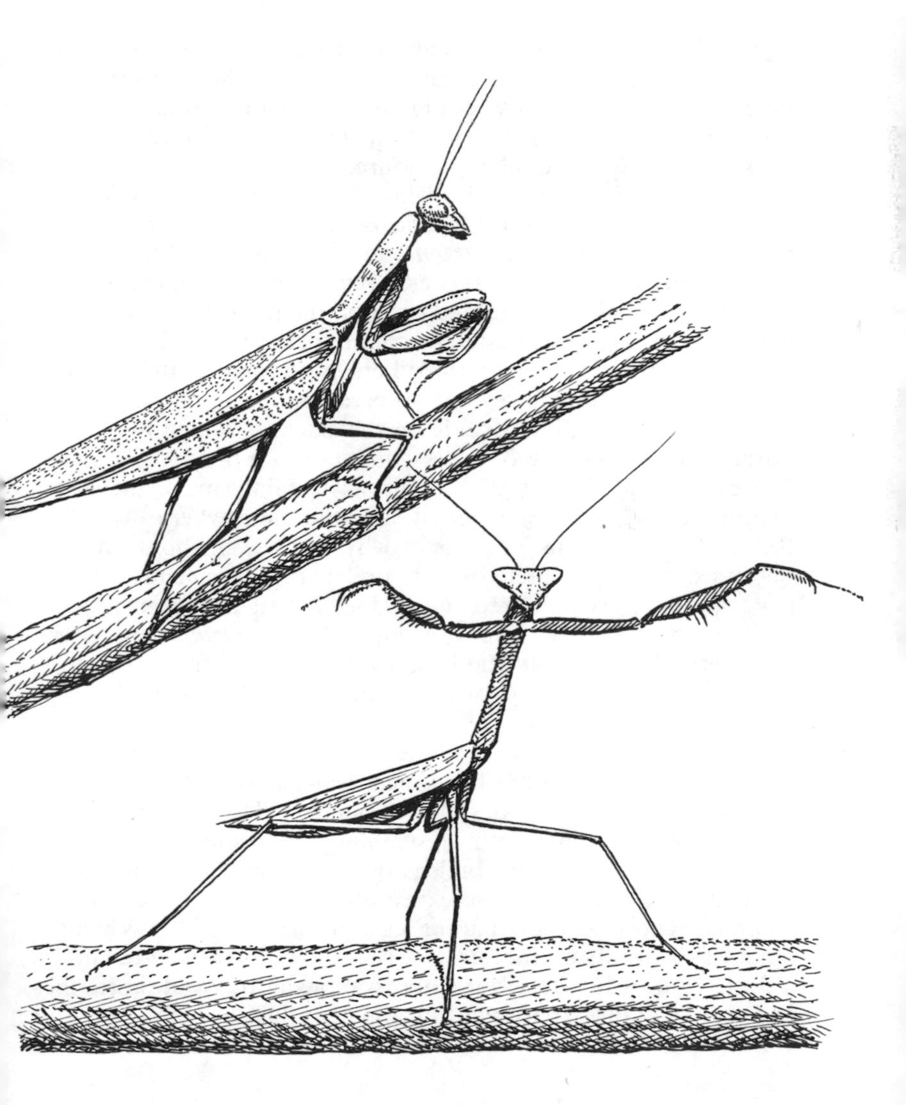

Figure 32. The majority of mantids are cryptically coloured, and sit and wait among foliage for insects to approach. Some mantids sit in flowers where insects are sure to arrive. The mantid is concealed by its remarkable similarity to the flower (see the mantid *Hymenopus* shown in figure 8). However, if the mantid looks like a flower, instead of sitting in one it can actually pretend to be a flower, as is possibly the case with the African devil's flower *Idolum diabolicum* shown here.

cryptically coloured: green when on leaves, and green with brown specks on bark. Some species resemble a dried, thorny twig, while others are conspicuously coloured. The latter species include *Hymenopus*, whose vivid coloration also serves for camouflage. This mantis sits on similarly coloured flowers and traps visiting insects (figure 8). Annandale, who observed *Hymenopus bicornis* under natural conditions in Malaya, found this species in the inflorescences of *Melastoma polyanthum* and was himself unable to distinguish between mantis and flower, even on close examination. He noticed that small flies alighted on both the petal-like legs and the body of *Hymenopus*. Although the mantis paid no attention to these, as soon as a larger fly joined the others, it was immediately trapped and eaten, even though several observers were standing watching. It is difficult, though, to decide on the extent to which the mantis attracts insects because of its resemblance to a flower. The petal-like extensions of the legs and thorax certainly make the insect appear flower-like even when it is sitting somewhere else. This being so, there seems no reason why the flower should not be dispensed with altogether. In fact, a related African genus, *Idolum*, is equally brightly coloured but it does not sit in flowers; it pretends to be a flower. The very large *Idolum diabolicum*, fifteen centimetres long without the legs, attaches itself to trees or bushes, often hanging from only two legs and stretches out its free legs like thorns or died twigs. The shin and foot (tibia and tarsus) are brown coloured. The thigh and the segment linked to the body (the hip, or coxa), on the other hand, bear leaf-shaped outgrowths, and these also occur on the sides of the abdomen. The prothorax bears a shield-shaped outgrowth, resembling that found in mantids which sit in flowers. The forelegs of *Idolum* are particularly conspicuous, and the coxae are extraordinarily big and are brightly coloured ventrally. The adjacent leg segments are green. When the animal sits with its normal posture (figure 32), it strongly resembles a flower. According to Muir's observations in the wild, butterflies and especially flies approach this apparent flower to examine it at close quarters. This is all that is necessary for the mantis to snap its

pincers on to the prey. *Idolum* is therefore a flower model in that it has a deceptive appearance to attract prey. This assumption is supported by Muir's attempts to produce similar artificial models. He simply attached brightly coloured pieces of paper to trees, and these models were approached by flies and sometimes beetles.

A further refinement is worthy of note, which is the aggregation of dark spots on the hind edge of the prothorax shield in *Idolum*. At a brief glance, these spots look like small insects eating voraciously. The spots are probably insect models that serve to attract insects, because Annandale noticed that more flies landed on a *Hymenopus* sitting alongside a flower after one had already landed. An extremely obvious black spot on the tip of the abdomen of *Hymenopus* is indistinguishable from a small fly even at fairly close range. Annandale assumes that *Hymenopus* virtually pretends that a fly has already landed on its abdomen in order to attract other small flies and eventually bigger ones as well. Wiesmann demonstrated recently that this interpretation is probably correct. Flies only perceive smells at close range, while at greater distances they are attracted to food sources by seeing that flies are already present on the food. There is then a kind of gregarious instinct, by which flies are attracted from some distance by stationary flies – even dead ones. Wiesmann set out two similar food-dishes, one containing ten dead house-flies. The dish containing dead flies attracted far more flies than the empty dish. This is named the flycatcher effect, because if a fresh flycatcher is suspended from the ceiling it can take a long time before a fly sticks to it, but as soon as the first lands, others quickly come. It is not necessary to have real flies: the same success can be achieved with black fragments of paper laid next to a food source or a fly-trap. The manufacturers of flycatchers could make them far more effective by covering them with black spots.

It would be reasonable to assume that the evolution of these mantids has passed from inconspicuous, cryptically coloured mantids sitting on bark or foliage to coloured species sitting in flowers and then finally to the devil-flower mantids such as *Idolum*. This assumption is supported by the behaviour of these insects.

As described above, normally coloured mantids and the coloured inhabitants of flowers such as *Hymenopus* hold the catching legs in the folded position when on the look-out. In contrast, *Idolum* spreads these legs wide apart, which is easy to interpret on functional grounds since only in this way do the flower colours on the inside of the coxae show properly. But the insect does not know this, so how has it evolved this aberrant posture? To answer this, it is essential to know that the same posture is shown by various species of mantis but for a different purpose – that of threat. This was investigated in fifteen species by Miss Crane in Trinidad, who found that several species threaten potential enemies with laterally extended, sometimes completely stretched, forelegs. This posture was never observed to be directed against a conspecific, in courtship, or in encounters between two individuals of the same sex. It was not even seen before a mantis struck or ate a conspecific. The response was elicited, for example, by the human hand, a rapidly moving pencil, and lizards. In some species the spreading of the forelegs in this threat posture exposes conspicuous colour-spots or even eye-spots, which are located either on the thorax or on the legs, and are normally invisible. The effect is often enhanced by erecting or spreading coloured wings or by displaying a coloured belly. (In the same way, the mantis shrimp *Squilla* spreads its catching legs in threat and exposes conspicuous colour-spots, which are normally hidden by the folded legs.)

It is interesting to note that this sudden display of vivid colour patterns is pure bluff in the case of mantids. These insects are unable to protect themselves effectively against lizards, birds and similar predators and they are perfectly edible. The threatening colour patterns are therefore not warning patterns. As far as is known, this threat posture does not correspond in form or colour with another offensive or inedible animal, and so it does not fall under the heading of mimicry. The threat posture nevertheless works. The animal's unexpected change confuses or intimidates a predator, which leaves the prey alone. The mantids thus protect themselves with an unfamiliar surprise effect. Only adult animals perform this behaviour and it is most common among females.

Idolum exhibits the expanded posture continuously, so that the flower-like coloration is always visible. The pattern would disappear if the legs were folded as in typical mantids. Furthermore, *Idolum* does not exhibit the threat posture (assuming that we are to keep this designation) only in response to a particularly threatening stimulus, as if it were an extraordinary fright-prone animal. (It is not known whether this species possesses other threat patterns.) The similarity to a flower may also lead potential predators astray. Typical mantids have to wait until insect prey chances to approach close enough. They must aim carefully and be able to aim in different directions, since the prey may come from any direction. *Hymenopus* has an easier task in catching prey, since it sits in the food-bowl to which the prey come of their own accord; the element of chance is removed. Finally, *Idolum* also removes the element of chance, and has at the same time disposed of the necessity to co-operate with a flower. This mantis does not have to aim particularly accurately, and does not need to perform the typical strike action, since insects are attracted to the ventral side of the head and into the most suitable position for trapping. This method is comparable to that already discussed for angler-fish. An exact investigation of the flower-model, the behaviour and the development of its features during life is still lacking for *Idolum*, so some doubts remain concerning the actual performance of its prey-catching mechanism.

Insect-luring plants

The higher plants, being immobile, have solved the problems of reproduction and dispersal in different ways. The male sex cells (or pollen) are transferred to the female sex cells by wind, water or animals, and the seeds are dispersed by the same methods. There are flying seeds, swimming fruits, sticky or burred fruits that become attached to animals, and edible fruit.

Wind and water are available free of charge and carry pollen and seeds over large distances, but the process is non-directional. The pollen may fall on barren ground and so may the seeds. The pollen, of course, must reach plants of the same species, and in order to guarantee this, the plant has to produce enormous quantities of pollen so that at least a proportion arrives at the female flower. Animals which move from one plant to another are more reliable messengers, but they are no better than postmen delivering circulars, for the next flower is not necessarily one of the same species. As long as the messengers seek out all available flowers without any form of selection, the plants are served no better than by wind or water.

The danger of misdirection is avoided, however, if different species flower at different times, thus more or less avoiding each other by temporal means. In addition, plants exploit the fact that animals profit from experience. An animal which has a favourable memory of a particular flower will search for further flowers of the same type. Many plants therefore have flowers which differ from others as much as possible, and each flower advertises itself in the most favourable manner possible. The large range of colour and form found in flowers offering nectar can thus be interpreted largely as a mutual contrast effect which renders it likely that the pollen-carriers will remain loyal to a particular species.

Some flowers show a very drastic way of avoiding competition with one another. After pollination they change colour and sometimes their odour as well and are then no longer visited by bees and bumble-bees, which are particularly loyal to their chosen species. The flowers of the germander speedwell *Veronica chamaedrys* are at first dark blue but turn purple on the evening of the first day when the nectar becomes scarce. Some orchids of the genus *Catasetum* immediately cease to emit an odour when they have been fertilised or when the anthers have shed their pollen.

Plants do not necessarily have to attract hordes of messengers. They can instead specialise in attracting particular messengers. We can thus distinguish flowers attracting bees, flies, diurnal moths, beetles, birds, and bats. Members of all these plant groups have specialised upon specific pollen-carriers and have developed structures specially adapted to the sense-organs and behaviour of the carriers. Flowers adapted for visits from herbivorous bats or fruit-bats in the tropics open only at night. Such flowers are black or white (bats are colour-blind), large and strongly built (bats are heavy and grip tightly with their claws), equipped with a fermenting odour (bats prefer over-ripe fruit) and suspended on long stems (bats are not very skilled at landing). An unusual amount of nectar is present (bats have a much greater stomach capacity than insects). Flowers directed at birds, on the other hand, flower in the daytime, have no odour, possess vivid colours and likewise have large amounts of nectar. Flowers intended for insects are small, possess various odours, produce much less nectar and have colours which are conspicuous to the insect eye. Since insects perceive ultra-violet light, many flowers have a large ultra-violet component in their coloration which we do not see. In addition, such flowers are often patterned with contrasting colour spots, or nectar-guides, which lead the insect to the nectar when it has once alighted on the flower. These nectar-guides are often coupled with odour-guides, which have a more intensive smell differing from that of the petals.

Nectar is not the only reward offered by plants to the messengers. Many insects eat pollen, and this too is produced by many plants. Some plants, such as *Cassia* species, have even developed special nutritive sterile pollen in addition to the normal form. The sterile pollen is offered on special anthers for the nourishment of visitors. Other flowers, those of orchids in particular, are equipped with protein-rich edible hairs or other edible tissues, which are likewise devoured by visitors. Flowers then, usually provide their guests with food; but some Brazilian orchids, for example, in the sub-family Catasetinae, have no nectar. Instead, glandular areas on the flowers secrete odoriferous oils. These flowers are visited by male *Eulaema* bees, and not by females as might be expected. Males of *Eulaema* species roughly the size of a bumble-bee collect the odoriferous oil in pockets on the hind-legs and use it to mark their courtship territories. These orchids are exclusively pollinated by these male bees.

Some plant signals designed to attract messengers must be learnt by experience by the animals, but there are also plants whose signals they already know. Although the plant uses these signals for other purposes, they have a particular significance for the insect messenger. The plants thus save themselves the reward for training, and parasitise other signals, that is, they produce an illusion. For this reason, we speak of deceptive flowers, although this name is not very useful since non-flowering plants also employ this trick. The knowledge of the plant signal may be innate to the insect, or it may be learnt in another situation; sometimes, both factors are involved. Kugler was able to demonstrate that freshly-hatched greenbottle flies *Lucilia*, blowflies *Calliphora* and flesh-flies *Sarcophaga* immediately head for glistening droplets (or droplet-dummies). The white flowers of the grass of parnassus *Parnassia palustris* contain five spatulate nectar petals bearing numerous finger-like processes, each with a glistening button. The buttons contain no nectar, but they still attract flies. This attractive effect is nevertheless legitimate, since two depressions in the upper surface of the odoriferous nectar petals do contain nectar. In contrast, the glistening secretory droplets on the glandular stems of the sundew *Drosera* constitute a wicked deception. The sundew is one of the insectivorous plants with which we shall deal later on.

Glistening droplets or droplet-dummies (pseudo-nectaries) constitute only a part of the signal patterns of flowers, for colour and odour play additional roles. The flies mentioned above show practically no response to colours when inexperienced, but experienced greenbottle flies respond strongly to colour. Kugler found that greenbottle flies and blowflies spontaneously prefer yellow and orange, but that this preference shifts to brown, purple-brown or charcoal in the presence of odours from faeces or decomposing matter. This helped to partially clear up an old dispute.

It had been known for some time that many malodourous flowers which attracted flies and dung-beetles have yellow, brown or red-and-black markings. The flower of *Diplocyanthus*, for example, is ash-grey. Together with their odours, these flowers are reminiscent of festering wounds, carrion or congealed blood. Flies did not appear to be particularly interested in these colours in earlier experiments because these had been carried out with odourless models. The new evidence indicates that colour is an important factor after all.

The carrion-flowers attract insects with their colour and odour under false pretences, since the dung-beetles and carrion flies are searching for rotting flesh as food and as a site for depositing their eggs. (It must be added that most flesh-flies are viviparous and deposit their larvae on rotting flesh.) Nevertheless the visitors usually find nectar which they can eat. The odour deception is so effective in *Stapelia* species, which have a smell similar to that of carrion, that blowflies even lay their eggs in the flowers. Some carrion-flowers even force their guests to the meal-table by luring them into a trap, as do cuckoo-pints and their relatives (*Arum*, *Auromatum*). These flowers are surrounded by large leaf-sheaths which are open at the top. The end of the inflorescence axis protrudes above from the sheath that surrounds its base and has a repulsive odour. At the very bottom of the chamber are numerous female flowers, which secrete a slimy fluid. Above these flowers, there is a wreath of downwards-pointing spines encircling the axis. Still higher up is a broad ring of male flowers, similarly topped by a wreath of spines. The stinking odour of this plant (largely NH_3) spreads over a very wide area because the plant develops temperatures up to 15°C greater than that of the environment. This heat results from a metabolic turnover unequalled in the plant kingdom. Normally, plants avoid the production of metabolic heat as much as possible, and energy from the oxidation of food is immediately used for useful chemical processes. At the time of flowering, however, the cuckoo-pint blocks this specific energy-absorption, as Meeuse recently demonstrated. It is possible that the heat not only increases the dispersal of the odour but also directly acts to attract insects. In Arctic zones, at least, nectar-eating mosquitoes (*Aedes*) frequently sit in the warmer flowers of the dryad flower *Dryas integrifolia* and even rest in flowers of the arctic poppy *Papaver radicatum*, which do not contain any nectar at all and which may attract insects solely because of the heat they produce. The increased temperature would increase the rate of development of both the plant and the visiting insects, which is an important factor in polar areas. Unfortunately, all that we know on this matter is derived from a few observations carried out by Hocking and Sharplin and no planned experiments have been conducted.

The odour of cuckoo-pint flowers, which is reminiscent of dung, urine, carrion or decaying blood, attracts flies and dung-beetles. The cuckoo-pint *Arum maculatum* particularly attracts the small owl midge *Psychoda*, which frequents places of human excrement. The insects land on the sheathing leaf or the axis, and both are so slippery because of the presence of oil droplets that the alighting insects slide down into the cup. The rings of spines prevent them from escaping. If the visitors have brought cuckoo-pint pollen with them, this adheres to the female flowers as the insects attempt in vain to climb past them to freedom. In the period of captivity, they eat the juice of the flowers. During the night, the male flowers mature and cover the insects resting below with pollen. The spines shrink, the exit is laid open and the visitors eventually creep out the following day. The insects then set off once again in search of carrion and at some time during the following day will probably end up in a neighbouring cuckoo-pint and will deposit the pollen at the right place. The cuckoo-pint produces its odour and heat during the midday period within a restricted phase of a few hours, when insects are most active, and this is governed by a substance produced by the male flowers six to eighteen hours before they reach maturity. The whole complicated mechanism and the time-schedule are admirably adapted to deceiving the visitors. Since the male flowers develop only after the female flowers, self-pollination is prevented.

Figure 33. The inflorescence of the cuckoo-pint (left, external appearance; right, opened up) consists of many hidden flowers. Insects that are attracted to the odour of carrion are forced to pollinate the flower by a rather underhand trick. Insects attracted by the carrion odour pollinate the female flowers and are trapped inside the inflorescence by rings of bristles until the male flowers mature. Only when the male flowers have matured are the insects liberated, freshly laden with pollen.

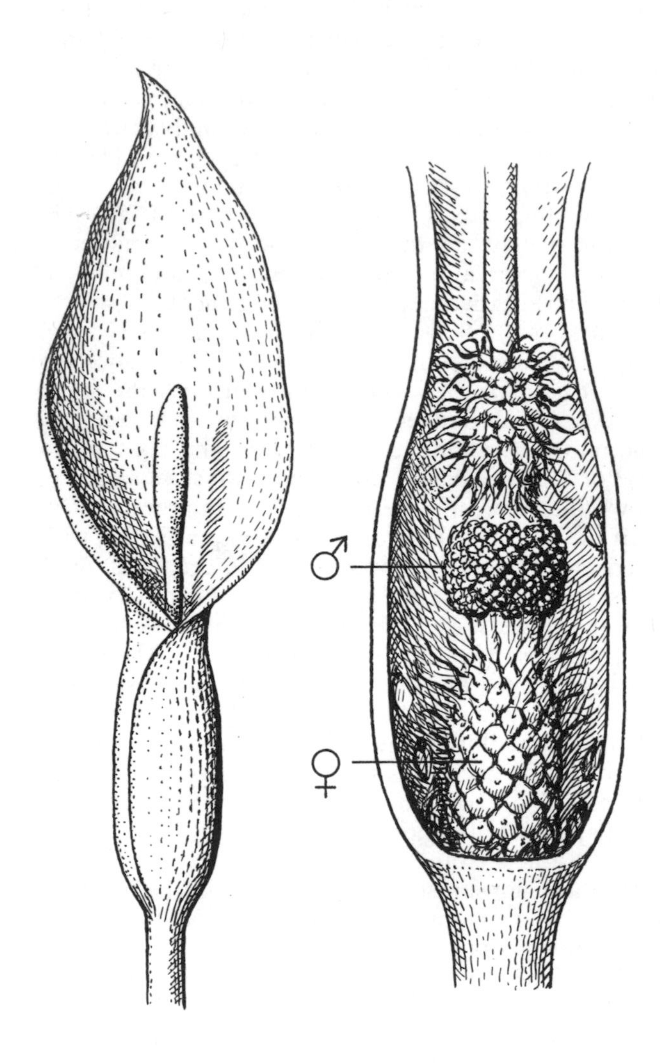

Similar flowers with a slippery trap are found among birthwort species (*Aristolochia*), some of which function as a light-trap on the basis of a transparent spot in the cup wall. Insects seek the exit at the transparent spot and are thus directed to the stigmas of the flower. The next day, an annular window and diaphragm lead the visitors to the outside, by which time they have been covered with pollen. These flowers also have a dung-like odour or smell of carrion. The well-known lady's slipper *Cypripedium*, an orchid, has a labium shaped like a wooden clog, which similarly acts as a trap. In this case, the insects can creep out again straight away, but only along particular, predetermined paths along which they must first rub against the stigma and then the anthers. The lady's slipper has no nectar or odour, and insects are attracted by the coloration of the flowers, with its promise of nectar.

In the plants discussed so far, nothing happens to the insects, even if they do not always find exactly what they are looking for. Some insectivorous plants, however, trap insects by means of flower signals and then digest them. The leaves of the famous venus' flytrap *Dionaea muscipula* are coloured red on the inside surface. If an insect lands on this surface, it touches one or more of the sensory hairs on the leaf and the two halves of the leaf snap together quickly. The spiny edges of the leaf interlock and the insect is dissolved with digestive juices. The pitcher-plants (*Nepenthes*, *Cephalotus*, *Sarracenia*, *Darlingtonia*) form jug-like structures from individual leaves. The opening may bear flower-like markings and in some cases carries a lid-like flap which has the appearance of a flower and presumably has the additional effect of keeping rain out. *Nepenthes* secretes nectar at the edge of the pitcher. If an insect seeking food lands on this apparent flower, it slips on the edge of the pitcher and falls inside. Below the slippery zone, there is a ring of gland-cells which secrete a protein-digesting enzyme. The lower section of the pitcher is filled with digestive fluid bearing the remains of deceived insects. This murder story is capped by the pitcher-plant spiders, which inhabit the upper zone of the pitcher in those species where the glandular field does not extend this far.

Figures 34 and 35. Some insectivorous plants possess specialised trap-leaves, which serve as dummy flowers and lure hungry insects. Below left: a leaf of the venus fly-trap *Dionaea muscipula*. Below right: a trap-leaf of *Nepenthes gracilis*; the sectional diagram opposite shows the fluid containing insect remains at the bottom, the glandular area which produces the digestive fluid in the middle, and a gland-free area occupied by the crab-spider *Misumenops nepenthicola* at the top, which preys on some of the attracted insects.

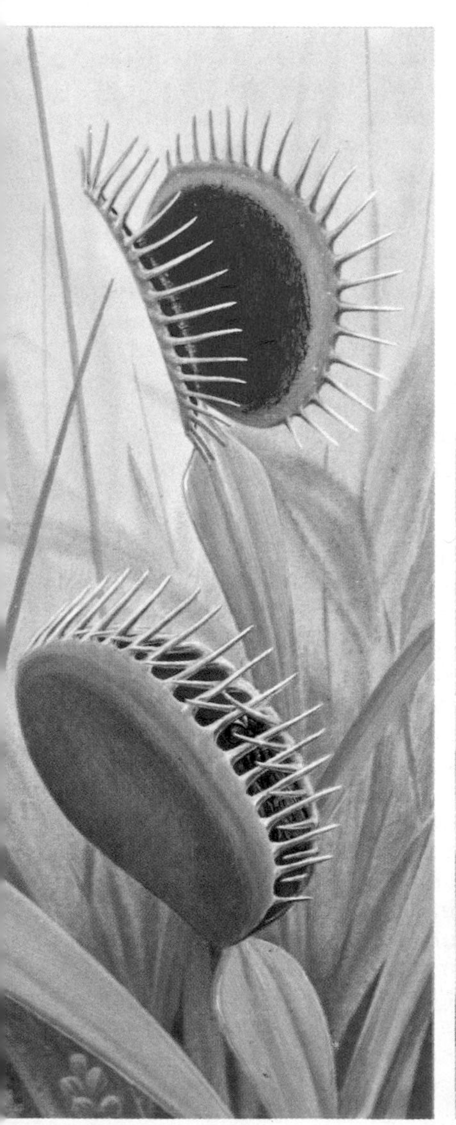

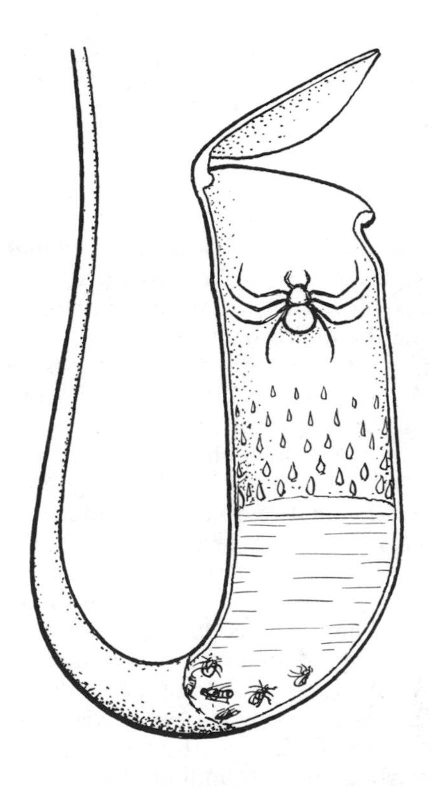

Misumenops nepenthicola inhabits *Nepenthes gracilis* in Borneo and *N. reinwardtaina* in Sumatra, while *Thomisus nepenthiphilus* inhabits the pitchers of *Nepenthes tabaica* in Sumatra. Both spider species are crab-spiders, which construct a safe scaffold with their silk across the slippery zone of the pitcher and then wait for insects which slip inside. Thanks to a special body covering, *Misumenops* can even retreat into the digestive fluid of the plant, between the insect remains, when danger threatens.

In addition to pollination, plants also attract insects for seed-dispersal, once again employing the same odours and colours. It has already been mentioned than many flowers pollinated by fruit-bats smell very much like fruits. Sometimes, the petals of the flowers are even fleshy and edible, as is the case with *Pachira insignis* and *Bassia latifolia*, and they are then eaten by the fruit-bats. Plants, in fact, evolved fruits in order to pursuade animals to eat them, and the seed inside the fruit is then dispersed by the animal automatically. Ants disperse plant seeds which are very hard but bear an edible appendage that is often rich in fat and vitamins. Larger animals frequently devour the entire fruit together with its seeds, and the seeds of many plants are so adapted to passage through the digestive tract of the animal that they will fail to germinate if they are not treated in this way. For instance, the seeds of the sausage tree *Kigelia* and those of the baobab *Adansonia digitata* will germinate only with difficulty, that is, with a large mortality rate and greatly increased germinal period, if they are not thus treated. If eaten by baboons and then ejected with the faeces the seeds germinate easily. Owners of haciendas in Ecuador have solved the problem of planting the seeds of the passion flower *Passiflora* along these lines. This plant is valued because of its fine-tasting fruits, but its seeds are difficult to sow untreated. The labourers in the field are given fruit to eat and are then ordered to defaecate at pre-determined spots on the field. A discovery made by Rick and Bowman on the small Galapagos tomato *Lycopersion esculentum* (*var. minor*) is particularly astounding. If the tiny seeds are sown, only 1 per cent develop, while removal of the outer husk by soaking the seeds for one hour in 2·6 per cent sodium hypochloride solution increases this to 71 per cent. What was surprising was the answer to the preliminary question as to who normally pre-treats the seeds. The giant tortoise *Testudo elephantopus* appears to be the animal responsible. At least, this is the only animal known whose digestive tract will naturally bring the seeds to 80 per cent successful germination. The seeds remain in the tortoise for about three weeks and can be carried quite a long way in this time.

Plants also exploit foreign odours in order to facilitate seed dispersal. Once again, the best-known examples concern carrion odours, like that given off by the stinkhorn *Phallus impudicus* in European woods. In this instance, the odour has been traced to the substance phenyl acetaldehyde, which has not yet been identified as an actual component of decaying flesh. But it is by no means necessary that model and mimic should employ the same substances as long as the signal-receiver reacts similarly to both; humans, for example react positively to saccharin, although it is not a sugar and has no nutritional value. The cap of a very young stinkhorn just emerging from its protective white sheath is covered with a thick green-black, shiny layer of spore slime (gleba). Blowflies, greenbottle flies and other insects are attracted by the carrion-like odour. The insects orient to the colour and sheen of the cap, land on the cap and immediately begin to eat. The tough spore slime is dissolved by the flies' saliva and is then completely decomposed in the digestive tract of the insects. The faeces of the flies consist largely of fungal spores. A few raindrops suffice to dissolve the faeces and to wash the spores into the soil. This has been investigated in detail by Schwemmer, who has finally given the lie to the oft-repeated statement that the flies smear themselves with the spore mass and carry the spores away on their bodies. The flies, in fact, do not even smear their feet.

There are some mosses which have flower-like structures to attract flies for the purpose of seed dispersal. The mosses *Splanchnum luteum* and *S.rubrum*, for example, use flies for the transmission of their sticky spores. The flies are attracted by a combination of a carrion odour and an optical signal, the latter being a display structure with red or yellow pigmentation developed from the sporangiophore beneath the spore capsule. The fungi and the mosses, of course, are non-flowering plants but they are still referred to as flower-mimics. Yet it remains uncertain, at least for the moment, whether the similarity to carrion-flowers, such as *Stapelia*, is based on the imitation of a particular flowering plant. Perhaps flower, fungus, and moss imitate carrion independently of one another. The green plants have become adapted to make use of red light for photosynthesis, which has the deepest penetration in the atmosphere and in water. Consequently, the chlorophyll that absorbs the sunlight is green in colour. As a complementary colour, red contrasts most with the ubiquitous green coloration of green plants. Apart from this, red and yellow have the further advantage that they are particularly clearly visible over large distances, an effect which is exploited in fog-lamps, for example. Thus, many plants produce flowers and fruits with red coloration as an adaptation to the sensory requirements of animals; it is not necessary to postulate that the fruits imitate flowers, or vice versa. The flesh of fruits, for example, corresponds to the nectar of flowers as a reward for the animals concerned. In this case, the animal is not deceived, and we are confronted with the same problem as that already encountered in the discussion of Müllerian mimicry. We do not yet know how nutritive the spore slime of the above-mentioned fungi is. But even if the slime has no nutritive function, so that we can speak of deception of the insects by the plant, it is still impossible to decide whether or not these pseudo-flowers would look just the same if no true flowers of similar appearance existed. Moreover, it is not clear how far the reactions of the insects are already adapted to such true flowers. The preference for serrated red surfaces could be the sole product of the structure and function of the insect eye, and the true flowers have probably adapted just as well to this as the false flowers of the spore-bearing plants. The only model which we can take for a mimetic carrion odour is carrion itself, but it is probable that all plants, whether flowering or spore-bearing, with the carrion odour are completely independent mimics of the model.

14 The origin of the cleaner mimic

One of the few cases of mimicry so far reported for vertebrates is found among marine fish. This provides an example of particularly close imitation of a model where morphology, coloration and behaviour are all covered by aggressive mimicry. The author had the opportunity to investigate this case in detail, so it will be considered here at some length.

The behaviour of the cleaner-fish The so-called cleaner symbionts rank among the most interesting relationships between different animal species. One animal frees another of externally attached parasites and occasionally damaged skin fragments. One oft-quoted example is the Egyptian plover *Pluvianus aegyptius*, which belongs to the pratincoles. African starlings of the genus *Buphagus* relieve many different mammals of their ectoparasites, and so do cattle egrets. Our starlings do the same for cows, while some farmyard chickens clean pigs. The series leads from chance cleaning to the professional cleaner.

Professional cleaners, especially in fish and crustacea, are particularly common in warm seas, and a summary has recently been provided by H.M. Peder. The term cleaner is applied to animals which remove and eat bacteria, ectoparasites, diseased and damaged tissue or excess food particles from fish and other marine animals. The customer is freed from unwelcome or sometimes harmful objects, while the cleaner obtains a good meal.

The cleaner which is of most interest in this context is the sea swallow *Labroides dimidiatus*, which is a wrasse. The fish swims with the aid of its pectoral fins, which beat like the wings of a butterfly. This fish lives in the Indo-Pacific ocean and occupies territories on coral reefs, usually in pairs. From our observations, only the dance and the behaviour towards other fish are of interest here. The term dance is applied to a particular swimming pattern, which is seen especially with young fish. The fish swims forwards slowly, repeatedly raising and dropping the hind-end of the body with the tail fin spread. This rocking locomotion makes the cleaner conspicuous to other fish. When other fish approach, the cleaner swims towards them and scours them. It glides over the surface of the customer, rapidly beating with the pectoral fins. If the customer does not stay still, the cleaner jabs it violently with its wide-open mouth and then continues with its work. The lower jaw of *Labroides* is forked like the claw of a carpenter's hammer and is used to prise parasites loose. The cleaner carefully scours the flanks, fins, cheeks, gills, teeth and sometimes even the throat of the customer. He plucks out anything that there is to pluck and leaves the customer only when the latter begins to fidget impatiently or when the work is really completed.

The ecological significance of the cleaner We now recognise 42 species of cleaner-fish in 14 families. In addition, there are various cleaning symbiotic relationships between fresh-water fish. Observations in aquaria (field observations are almost completely lacking in freshwater) have even shown associations between fish species from different parts of the world. Such cleaning associations develop in the aquarium only after the fish have acquired mutual coordination, thus demonstrating to the observer how such cleaning relationships may arise.

From the considerable list of ectoparasites (small crustaceans) living on fish, it can be concluded that the cleaning business is profitable. But we know of no cleaner which lives entirely from cleaning. Most cleaners eat free-living planktonic organisms and some clean only as young fish. Most well-known fish species are cleaning customers. They may be big or small, predatory (large perciform fish, morays) or non-predatory (mullets, mantas). The majority, the casual customers, are migratory fish, while the regular customers are territorial fish living in the vicinity of the cleaner. These fish go to the 'barber' with amazing regularity, often in the morning. Sometimes the fish have to wait their turn, and since they are usually mutually incompatible, they maintain an adequate distance from one another and wait restively. When one has been served, the others often jostle for service Morays, which are nocturnal or crepuscular, leave their retreats in broad daylight to visit the cleaner and then return to rest. The cleaners are quite busy since in addition to the regulars they also deal with other fish which chance to pass by. A number of divers, observing in turns, counted 300 cleaning customers visiting a single cleaner-fish within six hours! There are some reefs where thousands of cleaners live. The number of fish which collect there is extremely large, and the Pederson brothers were convinced by their observations that there are cleaning stations in the sea, rather like our spas, where large numbers of fish regularly pay visits. In order to test this, they selected two small, isolated reefs with an especially abundant fauna and counted the number of resident and non-resident fish over a certain period. They then removed all the known cleaners from the reef and continued to count. After a few days, the number of fish had shrunk considerably, and after two weeks there were only a number of territorially attached fish left. These fish bore numerous lightly covered fungal patches, loose fin fragments and abscesses. After a while, young cleaner-fish and cleaner-crustaceans from other areas settled on the reef and the normal fish population gradually reassembled. The new population consisted not of the previous inhabitants but of juvenile pioneers. It is now known that a number of profitable fishing-grounds represent cleaning stations. It had previously been a mystery that so many fish should assemble in these areas, since they were neither grazing nor spawning grounds.

The behaviour of the cleaning customer The most conspicuous behaviour of most cleaning customers is the trance-like condition they exhibit while being cleaned. Some even exhibit this state in advance, as if inviting cleaning. Breathing becomes shallow and irregular, the body sinks into an abnormal posture with the tail or the head drooping or the body rolling on to the side, and the balancing motions of the fins are suspended. Some species even change colour, and almost all gape and spread the gill-covers. The cleaners swim into the mouth and clean the inside and even swim in and out of the gills. Of course, the bigger the customer, the easier

Figure 36. Two cleaner wrasses (*Labroides dimidiatus*) in the act of cleaning a red snapper (*Lutianus sebae*). Top: a sabre-toothed blenny (*Aspidontus taeniatus*) attacking the tail fin, from which two semi-circular pieces have already been bitten. Bottom: the cleaner (above) and mimic (below) are shown in greater detail for comparison.

this is, as is shown particularly well by the large mantas. The fact that the cleaning customer actively responds to the cleaner can be seen from the fact that a fin which is being cleaned by the cleaner, or is simply close to the latter, is spread and held still. Angel fish (*Pomacanthus* species) and butterfly fish (*Chaetodon* species) usually spread only the gill-cover on the side where the cleaner is at work and then only when it comes into range of the head. The cleaner is even permitted to clean the extremely sensitive eyes.

Various fish species show different degrees of addiction to the cleaner. From my own experience, I know that *Odonus niger* (a large trigger-fish) easily becomes impatient and then slowly rotates about its longitudinal axis when cleaners take no notice. This usually meets with success. Many individuals of various territorial fish species remain still only for one particular cleaner and will visit him regularly. They will tolerate a strange cleaner only when their own cleaner disappears for a length of time. Injured and diseased fish often alternate from one cleaning station to the next and will also visit the same station several times a day.

Some cleaners treat their customers extremely roughly. They attempt to deal with all conspicuous areas, so that fish with small pearly spots have a rough time in an aquarium. The cleaner energetically attempts to remove these spots and suppresses resistance from the customer. I have always admired the strong nerves of the porcupine fish *Diodon*, whose skin bears small, spine-like outgrowths between the true spines. *Labroides* unceasingly attempted to tear off these outgrowths, and in so doing, shook the patient immobile victim back and forth. Aquarium observations of this kind help to demonstrate what stimulates the cleaner to work.

Even large predatory fish allow themselves to be cleaned, as mentioned above, and this is predominantly seen in the wild. Although these predators devour other fish of the same size, the cleaner (scarcely 10 cm long) invariably emerges uninjured from the throats of these beasts. This means that the cleaners are protected, although they are neither inedible nor capable of self-defence. A small occupational hazard is, nevertheless, involved in the work

of some cleaner species. Occasional finds of cleaners are made in the stomachs of other fish. From experiments which we have carried out, we can draw the conclusion that the behaviour of cleaners is very important when they are introduced to new surroundings. If they show a lack of confidence or flee from predators, they may be devoured. Normally, though, they make themselves conspicuous and draw the attention of other fish with their coloration and behaviour without endangering themselves.

The behaviour of the cleaner mimic At the cleaning stations where *Labroides dimidiatus* occurs, it is possible to find another fish which is almost indistinguishable from the cleaner in external appearance. This resemblance is particularly confusing when the fish is swimming and cannot be taken in the hand. If the fish is handled, it bites vigorously, something which a cleaner-fish never does. This other fish has powerful stabbing teeth in the lower jaw, a feature which has earned the name sabre-toothed blennies for the group to which it belongs. These are not members of the wrasse family, but a quite separate family. The fish resembling the cleaner is *Aspidontus taeniatus*. It is exactly similar in size, coloration and swimming behaviour and even exhibits the same dance as the cleaner. Fish which have had experience with the cleaner will also position themselves unsuspectingly in front of the mimic, showing the invitation posture for cleaning described above. They then receive a nasty surprise. The mimic approaches carefully and bites off a semi-circular piece of the victim's fin and eats it. The fish immediately jerks round after the jab, but the mock cleaner calmly stays put as if knowing nothing about it, and remains unmolested because of its cleaner's costume. Genuine cleaners, of course, sometimes nip the customer, and cleaning shrimps may even make small incisions in the skin with their chelae in order to extract embedded parasites. But the bite of the mimic *Aspidontus*, judging from the reaction of the victim, is much more painful. Fish which have been repeatedly bitten in this way become distrustful even towards genuine cleaners. The question that arises, then, is whether they are able to learn to distinguish between the cleaner and the mimic.

Adapting victims and the accuracy of imitation Most fish are unable to distinguish cleaner and mimic on a first encounter. The first encounter with the mimic must take place while the victim is quite young. We know from Randall's observations in the wild that *Aspidontus* preys largely on younger fish, while the older fish exhibit avoidance behaviour. It is thus fairly certain that the customer learns to distinguish between cleaner and mimic in the course of its life. It is very unlikely that the ability to discriminate develops automatically with age and is independent of experience, since adult fish kept in an aquarium also confuse cleaner and mimic. If these fish are kept with the mimics for a certain length of time, they eventually avoid both these and the genuine cleaners. Therefore they cannot distinguish between the two without having had experience of both and learning from experience. But what do they learn, and how? At first the customers learn to avoid sites at which they have bad experiences. Fish in general exhibit primary learning in the distinction of good and bad locations. If small crustacean food is presented in the aquarium in a test-tube, the fish at first vigorously snap at the food. They eventually learn that the food is unobtainable and abandon the test-tube. If the test-tube is then offered at another site in the aquarium, the fish immediately resume attempts to feed.

Fish which have been badly frightened by a predator in the wild avoid the site of the mishap for a long time, but do not avoid the predator. Thus, they first of all learn a negative reaction to a particular site and learn to avoid the common danger or obstacle only when they have encountered a number of similar experiences at other sites. Since *Aspidontus* itself is strongly territorial, all the fish resident in the neighbourhood soon learn to avoid its territory, without actually identifying it as a mimic. In anthropomorphic terms, they are only aware that one or other coral reef is occupied by an unpleasantly vicious cleaner-fish. Fish which are not acquainted with the area fall prey to the mimic especially easily. This means that species which are continuously on the move and which visit cleaning stations whenever the opportunity arises are preyed upon.

The mimic attacks only from behind and therefore usually bites into the tail fin. If a fish turns towards the mimic the latter turns away and awaits a new opportunity. The cleaner, on the other hand, approaches the customer from all sides, even from the front. The cleaning customer simply has to learn to turn its head towards any apparent cleaner. This is just exactly what some species do in the aquarium, although we do not yet know what happens in the wild. We still do not know how fish in the wild distinguish cleaners from mimics, but we do know that adults can distinguish and that they learn to do this. This means that the fish at first collects a wide range of experience with cleaners, mostly good and occasionally bad, for the mimic is less common than the cleaner, and this is the reason why fish still allow themselves to be cleaned despite bad experiences. In anthropomorphic terms, they search for some identifying characteristic in order to be able to see in advance whether a particular cleaner is reliable or unreliable. This means that the unreliable cleaner, that is, the mimic, must resemble the cleaner as closely as possible. Now if the deceived fish can continually collect information on the model and the mimic, then the perceivable differences between the two should gradually disappear. *Aspidontus* is in fact one of the most exact mimics we know. The model *Labroides dimidiatus* occurs as a number of local races within the area of distribution, with corresponding differences in coloration. Here and there, the cleaner is characterised by a small or large black vertical stripe at the base of the pectoral fins, while the cleaner population near Makatea in the Tuamotu archipelago bears an orange-red spot on the flanks. In every case, the local mimic population shows the same special coloration and is thus similar to the model in all areas, as was shown in an extensive survey in the wild carried out by Randall. This correspondence down to the finest detail provides support for the argument that recognition of the cleaner's costume is not an innate feature of the other fish but must be learned. Innately recognised signals are rarely so detailed. The only likely explanation previously advanced for particularly detailed imitation was based on the assumption that it was necessary in order to deceive a number of species, each of which concentrated on different characters. A rough correspondence would be sufficient for each species, but the sum effect would be exact mimicry. This hypothesis is very plausible, but no supporting evidence has yet been produced. The demonstrable learning capacity of higher animals should by no means be overlooked. Even if the recognition of the ground-pattern is innate, such learning capacity would dictate the development of supplementary refinements.

Learning competition with *Runula* Since the possibility of learning in the deceived fish is an important argument in this case of mimicry, I should like to present an even more drastic example. The predator is *Runula*, a relative of *Aspidontus*, and its behaviour provides important information about the origins of mimicry in *Aspidontus*, thus doubly justifying its mention here.

Runula is elongated, with horizontal black, blue and white stripes. This fish ambushes others from a concealed look-out and bites off pieces of skin in extremely rapid attacks. The skin is taken predominantly from the eye-region, where it is soft and free from scales. This fish resembles the cleaners only superficially, and I doubt whether other fish mistake it for a cleaner. I have kept *Runula rhinorhynchus* together with coral fish in very large aquaria, up to three cubic yards in volume. At first, *Runula* had an easy time, biting any fish which swam past the look-out position, but the others soon learnt to avoid this spot. *Runula* then attempted to sneak up to the other fish, by swimming around innocently and awaiting a suitable opportunity. The other fish then learnt to recognise *Runula*, previously only visible on brief excursions from the retreat. After a few days, wherever *Runula* swam in the aquarium the other fish maintained continuous surveillance. *Runula* does not attack from the front, and most of the victims soon learnt to exploit this, although some species did not, showing the variation in intelligence which is encountered. A marine Cichlid *Etroplus suratensis* was particularly preyed upon by *Runula* and soon did not dare to interrupt its continual watch on the fish for more than a few moments to feed. If I dipped a red rod into the aquarium to distract *Etroplus*' attention, it was immediately bitten. The fish soon learnt to ignore the rod, so that I could eventually jab and push it with the rod. The fish was in fact frightened, as could be seen from its change in colour, but did not move from the spot and observed *Runula* all the more carefully. There was good reason for this, since *Runula* had also learnt that the rod distracted the attention of this fish. *Etroplus* did not dare to flee from the rod until several days after I had removed the predator from the aquarium. Small Pomacentrid fish belonging to the genus *Abudefduf* were particularly observant of *Runula's* movements. Since *Runula* is almost entirely dependent upon fish skin for food, the predator was forced to find some means of approaching its victims. At first, *Runula* attempted to sneak up under cover of the substrate or the turbulent water-surface and would then dart upwards or downwards towards its intended victim, but the latter also became accustomed to this. They were regularly distracted when food was dropped into the aquarium, however, and *Runula*, ignoring this food, would rapidly enter the cloud of particles and lie in wait for the approaching fish. The most impressive trick of all was to make use of another fish as a screen. A clown fish (genus *Amphiprion*), an inhabitant of sea anemones, was exploited for this purpose. For some unknown reason, *Runula* never attacked fish of this kind, and so they showed no avoidance behaviour. In addition, these fish are regarded as harmless by all other occupants of the aquarium and could approach the latter without difficulty. *Runula* thus began to swim closely alongside the clown fish and would then suddenly spring out at the victims from cover, nearly always with success.

This competition in attack and defence is a very clear indication of the extent to which fish learn to notice the behaviour of other species when this is important for their survival.

Derivation of the mimetic characters of *Aspidontus* We can take the cleaner *Labroides dimidiatus*, the model for *Aspidontus*, as a basis for discussion of the origins of mimicry in this case. Both fish and humans confuse *Aspidontus* with the model because both have the following in common:

1. the habitat
2. the drive to approach other fish
3. body-size
4. shape
5. coloration
6. swimming behaviour
7. the dance

By carrying out an exact comparison with related species, it is possible to determine which of these characters were already possessed by *Aspidontus* and which have arisen through approximation to those of the model. This involves the assumption that the most widely distributed characters, also occurring in non-mimetic species, are closest to the ancestral form. One must, of course, take into account the individual specialisations in the species under comparison.

1. *The habitat.* Apart from a few exceptions, most Blenniids and their relatives are inhabitants of shallow waters on coasts and reefs – the same type of habitat as that occupied by the cleaner. Several species actually occur in close association with the cleaner on coral reefs. *Aspidontus* was therefore not forced to change its habitat in order to become a mimic, for it was already pre-adapted.

2. *The drive to approach other fish.* Most relatives of *Aspidontus* are predatory and live on small marine organisms, such as Crustacea. Any sufficiently large marine animal bearing small Crustacea on its body surface could easily represent a neutral substrate. Similar behaviour has been observed with many small fish, which will even choose large objects as a home base without distinguishing between immobile objects such as rocks, or moving objects such as mats of seaweed, tree-trunks, ships or large fish. One can assume that the habit of eating fish skin shown in *Runula* evolved via the habit of

hunting small Crustacea (possibly ecto-parasites) on the surface of fish. Apart from this, *Runula* does not restrict its attacks to fish, but also samples the legs of divers. The sudden attack and rapid biting is typical of *Runula* and *Aspidontus*, although they may sometimes attack more slowly and sometimes take entire prey. Only *Runula* and *Aspidontus* direct these attacks at fish. These two species are so closely related that they were at one time placed in the same genus. *Runula* is more strongly specialised for eating fish than *Aspidontus* and obtains its food in a different way, as described above. One may assume that the behaviour shown by these fish was exhibited by the ancestors of *Aspidontus*. The drive to approach other fish must also have been present early on, even if restricted to the relatives of *Aspidontus*.

Both *Runula* and *Aspidontus* attack fish from behind. *Runula* aims at the front, towards the eye, and bites away pieces from the body surface, whereas *Aspidontus* aims at the hind-end and bites lumps out of the edge of the fin. We know of no predecessors leading to this specialisation.

3. *Body-size*. The blennies are, in general, no larger than the cleaner, and are thus naturally suited in body-size for the role of mimic.

4. *Shape*. All blennies are elongated and somewhat flattened laterally, and the fins are usually similar in position and shape to those of the cleaner. There are exceptions here as well, but these represent later specialisations not present in the ancestors of *Aspidontus*. Thus the trunk and body shape were also pre-adapted.

This does not apply to the head. The wrasses, which include the cleaner *Labroides*, have a pointed head with laterally situated eyes, whereas most blennies have a blunt head, with the eyes almost dorsal and often protruding. As with a number of other fish families, this is a result of the method of locomotion: blennies are poor swimmers and cannot glide round obstacles, so they must plot their course in advance. In addition, they frequently leave their lairs on rocky coastlines and must therefore be able to orient accurately. But the *Runula-Aspidontus* group are particularly able swimmers and have a noticeably tapering head. No other species has such a pointed head as *Aspidontus*, and this must be interpreted as a further specialisation as a mimic.

5. *Coloration.* The basic coloration of *Aspidontus* is not greatly different from that of the cleaner and its relatives, since all are free-swimming fish living in open water and thus carry the characteristic light and dark horizontal stripes. The details can of course show a great deal of difference, as can be seen even among the close relatives of the *Aspidontus* group. The number of horizontal stripes varies and so does the ground-colour. The black longitudinal stripes of *Aspidontus* must therefore be regarded as an old family character, and the ground-colour was presumably also present before the specialisation as cleaner-mimic occurred. Nevertheless, both features have approximated to those of the model.

There is an additional complication, however, because blennies have a pronounced ability to change colour. This effect is actually reduced in the *Runula-Aspidontus* group in comparison to the other species, but within this group *Aspidontus* shows the most marked colour change. The four colour-patterns illustrated on page 170 for *Aspidontus* are linked by transitional phases. Only the colour pattern (b) is in agreement with that of the cleaner, and the others are distinctly different. The colour phase (a) (black dorsal fin, and black back) is characteristic of animals without a territory, or of those defeated in a fight, which show exploratory swimming. Colour-pattern (c) (black markings largely disrupted) is seen with animals involved in frequent fights with conspecifics or other species while maintaining a territory, as long as they are not subordinate. Colour-pattern (d) is typical of severely frightened animals, which press themselves into a handy crevice and remain immobile. The more belligerent an animal is, the greater the dissolution of the black markings. The converse applies to an increase in the tendency to flee. The result is that an *Aspidontus* in possession of a territory and free from threatening rivals, which is hungry and ready to bite, will show a condition intermediate between flight and attack when confronted with a fairly large fish rather than a rival. The

Figure 37. The mimic *Aspidontus taeniatus* alters its coloration with its state of motivation. It is confused with the cleaner wrasse only under specific conditions – when it exhibits the colour pattern (b). The colour patterns signify the following states: frightened and driven to defence (a), self-confident and prepared to attack (b). actively fighting (c), greatly frightened (d).

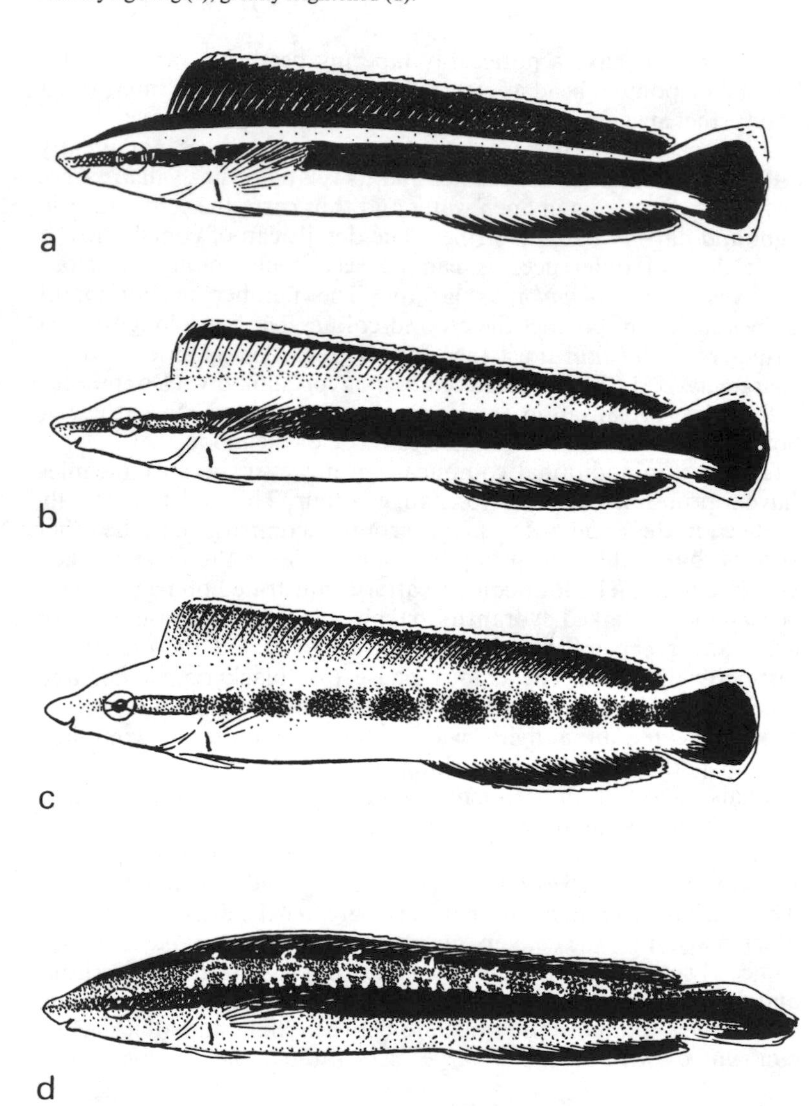

corresponding colour-pattern lies between the two extremes (light and dark) and therefore agrees with the pattern (b). The same can be observed with some blennies which do not show mimicry. The cleaner costume nevertheless appears more frequently in *Aspidontus* than expected, and so represents an adaptation toward mimicry.
6. *Swimming behaviour*. The blennies swim in various ways, depending on their specific weights. The forms that swim near the bottom have greatly reduced swim-bladders, are markedly heavier than water, and can swim only by means of powerful wriggling motions. The blennies originally possessed a typical swim-bladder, which can still be found in the larvae and is in fact retained in the adult *Aspidontus*, *Runula*, and the near relative *Petroscirtes*. The latter swims with amazing elegance, both backwards and forwards, and can hover almost motionless in open water. *Runula* is somewhat heavier and must either perform continual wriggling motions with its body or maintain very rapid motions of the pectoral and tail fins in order to stay in one spot. *Runula* is markedly unbalanced by a heavy tail and usually exhibits an oblique posture in the water. *Aspidontus* is roughly intermediate between the two, being free from the necessity to wriggle, thanks to the ability to advance solely by use of the pectoral fins, and yet shows a strong tendency to sink at the tail. All three wriggle when they are in a hurry, but otherwise often rely upon the pectoral fins. The body is held stiff and wriggling is suspended when the fish is confronted with danger. Thus, swimming with the pectoral fins is typical of the cleaner and is present in *Aspidontus* as one of several possibilities, representing a further pre-adaptation towards mimicry of the cleaner. The mimic makes use of this swimming motion mainly in conflict situations, for example when hungry and close to a large prey fish. In this way, *Aspidontus* follows the swimming pattern of the cleaner in just the right situation. As with the colour change, the range of conflict inducing the behaviour is widened so that swimming with the pectoral fins is the commonest motion in *Aspidontus*.
7. *The dance*. All the blennies discussed display a marked posture to conspecifics. Depending on the species, the dorsal fin may move up

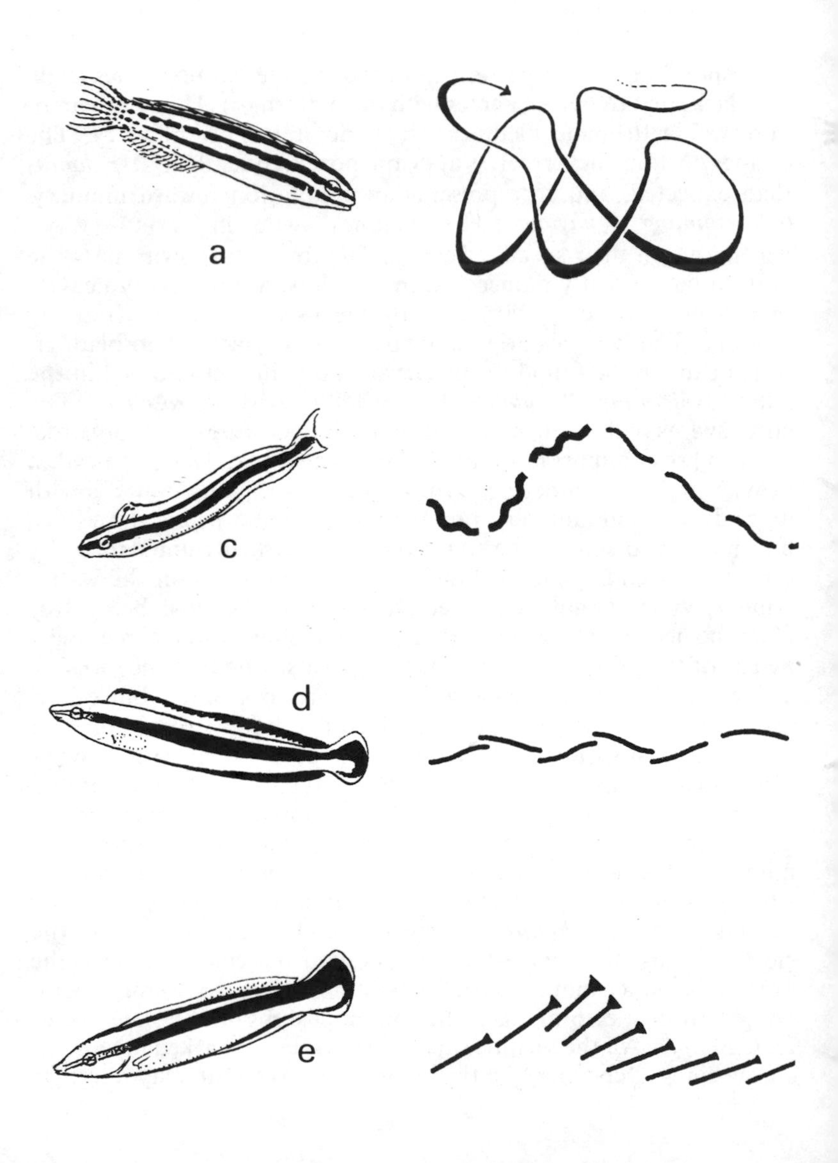
a
c
d
e

Figure 38. *Aspidontus* also mimics a conspicuous behaviour pattern shown by the cleaner. These sketches of movement patterns show the dance of the cleaner *Labroides* (e), its imitation by *Aspidontus taeniatus* (d) and the predecessors of this imitation dance in its closest relatives, the threat dance of *Runula rhinorhynchus* (c), the courtship dance of *Petroscirtes temminckii* (a), and the threat swimming behaviour pattern of the latter species (b).

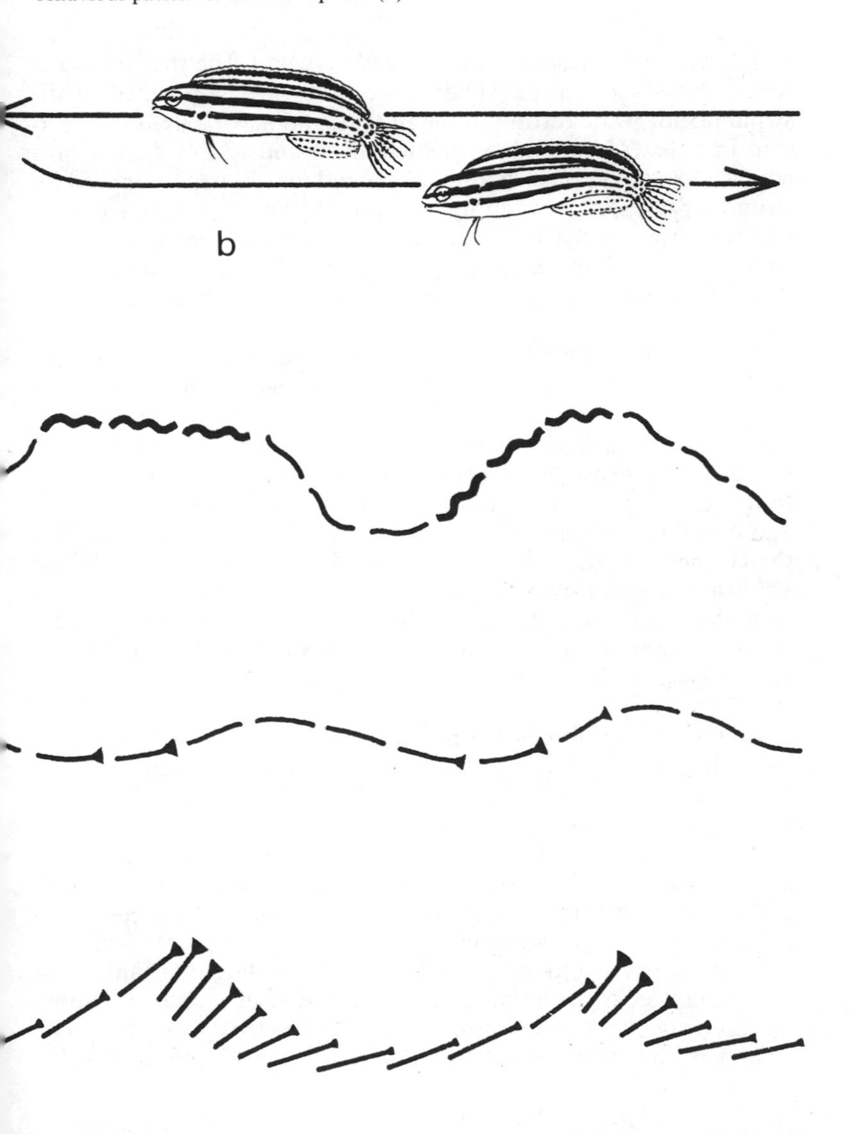

and down, or the head or anterior end may nod. The rhythm of the movements also varies. The movements are performed while swimming or while resting in the retreat, and may be used in courtship or threat. Nodding originated from and is still shown in a conflict between approach and retreat and may be superimposed on swimming, creating a wagging locomotion. The movements vary in meaning from genus to genus, and the form is probably an old pattern which later acquired its significance independently in different groups, that is, it gradually became restricted to specific situations.

This does not apply to *Aspidontus*. Nodding and nod-swimming in this species have become ritualised to a rigidly fixed signal, but they can occur in all types of situation, that is, they do not have a particular meaning. *Aspidontus* will nod to a piece of wood just as well as to a conspecific and responds in the same way to a large or restive prey fish. If nodding is performed while swimming, the tail and dorsal fins are spread – as in most conflict situations – so that the cleaner coloration is fully displayed. The hindquarters, which are heavier, sink down further and cover a more extensive wavy path than the nodding head. The entire fish bears an amazing resemblance to a dancing cleaner, although the tail is not swung upwards and the head leads in the wavy locomotion.

Conclusion If all the individual features are collected together, even the unspecialised proto-*Aspidontus* can be seen to have possessed many of the characters typical of *Labroides*. Body-size and form show close correspondence to those of the cleaner. The drive to approach other fish must have been present, although it is impossible to prove this. The variable characters of coloration and mode of swimming by chance approach those of the cleaner in the presence of fish suitable as prey, and a locomotor pattern reminiscent of the cleaner's dance occurs in conflict situations.

If we now consider a fish customer which visits a cleaner station, we can imagine a fish swimming around expectantly which bears a certain resemblance to *Labroides*. If another fish approaches, the motivation of the waiting fish to flee is raised. In combination with the motivation to attack produced by hunger, a conflict situation is produced and the waiting fish swims along a wavy path. But this motion, which is not situation-specific in proto-*Aspidontus*, has a particular significance for the cleaning customer. If the customer has had previous experience with *Labroides*, it has learnt that a similar motion is characteristic of the cleaner. Any doubts are thus reduced and the customer adopts the invitation posture for cleaning. This is just the opportunity for proto-*Aspidontus* to take a bite.

Such behaviour still occurs at the present time and can be observed in the wild and in the aquarium. The present-day *Aspidontus*, of course, resembles the cleaner much more closely than did proto-*Aspidontus*. Since the customers learn and seek out characters which enable them to distinguish between reliable and unreliable cleaners, the most successful *Aspidontus* individuals are those which are the most confusing to the customer. This steers the further development of the mimic in a particular direction determined by the characteristics of the cleaner. The mimic thus comes to resemble the model more and more closely, so that even racial variations are imitated.

The mimic which is most successful is the one which achieves the most bites on a customer. In contrast to the predators considered earlier, which devour the lured victim (angler-fish) or attach themselves to it (glochidia, trematodes), *Aspidontus* has the opportunity to deceive the same victim more than once, despite the victim's previous experience with it. As can be seen from observations in the wild, the mimic is only successful to a degree, since older experienced cleaning customers can distinguish the mimic from the model. The mimic thus depends largely upon young fish. From this we can conclude that even today selective pressures operate to increase the similarity between *Aspidontus* and *Labroides* as regards those characters which permit the customer to distinguish between the two. We are therefore able to predict the direction which further evolution will take, although we have no way of testing the validity of this prediction.

Imitation of *Labroides* has a double advantage for *Aspidontus*. First, the mimic is protected against predators which leave the model alone. It has already been explained that this immunity depends partly upon behaviour of the cleaner, and so behaviour must also be imitated by the mimic. Secondly, *Aspidontus* is able to attack other fish more easily with its deceptive cleaner's costume. This is the first time that it has been possible to trace back the individual characters, especially behavioural ones, of a mimicry pattern to their origin.

If it is true that blennies have a number of features in common with the wrasse group and are thus pre-adapted as mimics, it should be expected that other members of the blenny group might mimic other known species of wrasse species which act as cleaners. Observations in the sea actually support the suspicion that such mimic-model pairs exist.

15 Aggressive mimicry involving two species

All the cases of mimicry so far discussed are extremely difficult to investigate since a mimicry system usually includes different species. Some of the examples just dealt with include several species of animals and even plants. These organisms have different habitats and habits and only come together occasionally, often by chance. It is therefore not possible to discover easily whether, for example, the imitation is worthwhile, whether the organism can exist just as well without mimicry, how the imitation, if such it is, arose, and so on. If we want to know, for instance, whether the coloration of hover-flies, hornet moths or longicorn wasp-beetles and similar animals is advantageous because of the similarity to offensive, inedible insects, and the effect of this on insectivorous animals, then it is not enough to know how often an insectivore encounters the model and the possible mimic and how often it reacts; we must first of all know which insectivore is most important. But it is in cases of this kind that we have a particularly large number of insectivores to take into account, for instance frogs, toads, lizards, many bird species and insectivorous mammals. We can assume that each insectivore reacts in a slightly different manner, concentrates on different features of the prey, and employs different hunting techniques. The overall advantage gained by a species mimicking a wasp is thus composed of a number of subsidiary advantages depending on the particular predator. This is a reasonable assumption, but it does lead to a situation where one is tempted to attribute all the characteristics of the mimic to the function of mimicry. This gets us nowhere, and if one intends to provide answers to the various questions, then systematic observations are necessary. This in particular means that one must predict the encounters between the relevant species so that one knows *what* to observe.

The case of mimicry in cleaners takes us a long way, because cleaner and mimic occur in the same area, and encounters with cleaning customers occur so frequently that it is possible for an observer to make records. The same applies to carnivorous plants and those with putrescent odours. The model of the carrion-plant can equally well be controlled, although this is somewhat more difficult with the pitcher-plants. In all cases, it is possible to conduct experiments with the animal presumed to be deceived by the mimic. One can test the effect of various objects on its sensory apparatus and conduct experiments with models. Nevertheless, the conclusiveness of such experiments is dependent upon the degree of certainty with which the signal receiver has been identified. One must be sure that the sign stimuli investigated in the laboratory also play a role under natural conditions, because the same species may react differently to the same stimuli in different situations. It is known, for example, that the grayling (*Eumenis semele*) can perceive and distinguish colours when hungry and searching for blossoms, but that when sexually motivated and searching for a female, the male does not react to colour differences at all and behaves as if he were colour-blind. There are thus two main sources of difficulty in the study of mimicry. First, there are too many species involved in individual mimicry systems. Secondly, the situations in which the signal receiver encounters the supposed models and mimics are not known well enough. There are simply too many species and too many possible situations.

The fact that representatives of separate animal orders or classes may be involved in one mimicry system is a particularly disturbing factor in attempts to reconstruct the evolution of the systems. It is necessary to investigate as many species of model, mimic and signal receiver as possible and a search must then be made for the original characters of the signal transmission or the associated reactions. Once again using the example of the wasp, it would be necessary to compare the wasp species, the bee species and the hornet species and to follow this with a comparison of hover-flies with other flies, hornet-moths with other hawk-moths and longicorn wasp-beetles with other longicorn beetles. Finally, it would be necessary to compare the possible predators (spiders, frogs, toads, lizards, birds, small mammals) in their reactions to such stimuli in order to determine whether they must learn the warning colours, and if so, how they do it. Such data would have to be compiled for each individual case of mimicry. This is possible in principle, but so far we know so little about even the commonest animals that these specialist questions must remain unanswered for some time to come.

This sounds rather discouraging, but there is a simple expedient and that is to select cases where only a few species are involved. Even three would be too many, and yet a mimicry system must, by definition, contain at least three members – model, mimic and signal receiver. The only hope is that now and then more than one of these members may belong to the same species. Fortunately, three possible combinations exist in which two members are conspecifics. The first possibility is found with bees and wasps, where the non-poisonous drones are to be regarded as mimics of females equipped with a poisonous sting. The second possibility, where the mimic and the deceived signal receiver belongs to the same species is provided as an introduction to the next chapter. The commonest situation, however, is where the model and the deceived signal receiver belong to the same species.

Cuckoos

It is a well-known fact that the common cuckoo *Cuculus canorus* lays its eggs in the nests of other birds, and that the unwitting foster-parents hatch and raise the young cuckoo. The most common foster parents of the cuckoo are wagtails, garden warblers, red-backed shrikes, reed warblers, tree pipits, meadow pipits, fieldfares, redstarts, bramblings, black redstarts, whitethroats and hedge sparrows. Cuckoo eggs have actually been found in the nests of 180 other species of bird, but this figure includes species in whose nests cuckoo eggs are found but seldom and which do not rear the young cuckoo. The female cuckoo thus occasionally lays an egg where the offspring has no chance of survival. Some people have explained this by saying that the pregnant female is forced to do it, but this does not agree with the known facts. Early naturalists considered the problems that the cuckoo has to contend with when laying its egg in the closed nest of the wren or in the narrow nests of hole-nesting birds. The female is too big to squat in these nests and lay her egg directly, and so a special indirect method must be used. The female gets round the problem by laying the egg on the ground, picking it up in her beak and carrying it to the nest of the host bird. But since the cuckoo is able to do this, why does a pregnant female sometimes choose an unsuitable nest? She could surely pick up the egg in her beak, even when the egg is located in the wrong nest, and carry it to a better site. It has not yet proved possible to answer this question.

A suitable nest must not only belong to a pair of birds which will raise the young cuckoo but must also contain some eggs laid by the female host. For this reason it is necessary to understand the behaviour of the host birds. If the host has not yet laid eggs and then finds a strange egg in the nest, the nest is often abandoned. If, on the other hand, an extra egg is added after laying, the host does not notice, or is only slightly disturbed, possibly because the birds involved are unable to count. However, it is known that after the cuckoo lays an egg, she often carries off one or more of the host's eggs in her beak and then eats or discards them. If the host cannot notice a change in the number of eggs, this should be unnecessary, and if the cuckoo carries off more than one egg then the number of remaining eggs is in any case wrong.

The cuckoo lays only one egg in each host nest, a feature of great importance. The young cuckoo hatches after a very short incubation period of 11 to 13 days, while the host birds hatch after 13 to 15 days. The cuckoo therefore hatches shortly before or at the same time as its nest-companions. The young cuckoo, still naked and blind, treats its stepbrothers and stepsisters in a most ungentle manner: regardless of whether they have hatched or not, they are thrown out of the nest. To achieve this, the young cuckoo presses sidewards and backwards beneath the egg or fledgling and loads it on to its back. The load is then held in place with the wing-stumps, while the cuckoo, pushing with its head, climbs backwards on to the ridge of the nest and drops its burden overboard. This instinctive act begins 10 hours after hatching and ends after 4 days. So it is not really necessary for the mother to carry off an egg belonging to the host to ensure that her offspring get enough to eat, because the young cuckoo automatically receives everything brought by the host parents. We do not know why the cuckoo carries away one or more eggs, but it possibly results in the host being left with an optimal number of eggs to brood. All the host eggs cannot be carried away, since the foster-parents would then abandon the nest. The reason why the female cuckoo lays only one egg per nest is that the young cuckoo throws out all other occupants of the nest; and two female cuckoos cannot use the same nest since the two cuckoo fledglings would try to eject each other. Considered another way, the drive to eject all nest-companions was able to develop only where a single young cuckoo occupied a nest and could get rid of all food-competitors without endangering members of its own species. A drive of this kind would be eliminated if the fledgling were surrounded by siblings. It is interesting to note that the fledgling of the honey-guide *Indicator minor*, another brood-parasite related to the barbet bird and the woodpeckers, kills off its stepbrothers and stepsisters with dogged thrusts and jabs with its hooked, dagger-like beak.

The ejection of the foster-parents' offspring is very important for the young cuckoo, since it grows much larger than its foster-parents and requires an enormous amount of food. The hosts, however, perform this task readily and pay no attention to their own, ejected offspring, even when these are obviously visible lying close to the nest. Instead, they avidly feed the young cuckoo and continue to do so even when the cuckoo is bigger than themselves. The reason for this is provided in the experiments discussed below, which also explain the behaviour of the other brood-parasites to be discussed later.

The feeding signal One of the features of instinctive behaviour in animals is the prompt response to specific sign-stimuli. Stimuli or combinations of stimuli elicit specific behavioural responses in the stimulus-receiver and a special stimulus-filtering apparatus inside the animal distinguishes between different environmental stimuli. In a given situation, the animal selects certain characteristics such as danger from an aerial predator, a rival close at hand, etc., and then shows the appropriate behaviour, such as flight or threat. For example, the German word *Grünschnabel* (green-beak), usually used to refer to young upstarts, is derived from the fact that young birds possess a greenish or yellow border of skin along the edge of the beak. When the fledgling begs food by gaping, this skin has the form of a yellow diamond when seen from the front. For the adult bird, this colour-signal means, 'Please deposit food here'. In fact, the bird will cram its stock of food into any yellow-rimmed hole, even when this is made of cardboard. In many cases, the coloration of the interior of the beak and of the tongue is equally important, but the presence of the neck, abdomen, wings or legs of the young bird is immaterial. The adult can perfectly well afford to ignore these other details and concentrate upon a response to the simplified signal, since it is hardly likely to find a beak sitting all alone in the nest. Sometimes, however, a young bird fails to gape when the parent returns to feed. If this occurs repeatedly, another mechanism may be set into operation: fledglings which do not gape are regarded as dead and are removed from the nest by the parents.

The fine adaptation of these responses to normal conditions, and the parents' lack of insight into why these responses are made, was recognised by Professor Koenig. He attempted to breed bearded tits in cages and found that the offspring never survived because the parents ejected them from the nest. The unexpected cause was quite simple: bearded tits usually experience difficulty in collecting enough food for their young, which are consequently never satiated and always gape when the parents arrive. However, under caged conditions, the parents were provided with sufficient food at a short distance from the nest. They were thus able to achieve something impossible in the wild – they satiated their offspring, which then stopped gaping for a time. This situation had not been catered for in the behavioural structure of the species, and the parents ejected the overfed young from the nest as if they were dead. Careful feeding immediately eliminated this practice so that it then proved possible to breed the birds without further loss. Even in the normal nest, the greatest amount of food is given to the fledgling which begs most. In other words, the intensity of the feeding reaction is proportional to the strength of the begging stimulus. A weak fledgling is in a sorry state, for it begs weakly and is by-passed; it then becomes even weaker, begs more weakly and rapidly succumbs.

The young cuckoo exploits this behaviour in reverse. Its enormous red gape stimulates the foster-parents to continual feeding. The begging signal is utterly irresistible for the parents, especially since the young cuckoo does not close its beak while swallowing and therefore transmits the stimulus signal without interruption. When the young cuckoo leaves the nest after about 3 weeks, at which stage it is still fed by its parents, even strange adult birds and newly-fledged juveniles of other species will feed it. For this reason, the famous ornithologist Oskar Heinroth referred to the cuckoo as a 'vice of its foster-parents', since they really do respond like addicts to this supranormal sign stimulus. A further example of this effect will be provided shortly.

Sign stimuli characterising the egg The existence of supranormal stimuli was demonstrated with birds' eggs at a very early date. The best-known example is that of the oyster-catcher, which unfailingly broods the biggest egg available. If a giant egg is placed on the nest, the oyster-catcher stubbornly attempts to brood it, even when it is unable to sit on the egg and slides off. The normal eggs alongside are ignored, and once again, the response is made to the strongest sign-stimulus. In this case, such behaviour is normally harmless, since the oyster-catcher never lays eggs as big as those that it actually prefers.

Size is not the only decisive factor, however. Many birds respond to a number of other egg features. The most important of these are the colour and pattern of the egg-shell, which varies from species to

Figure 39. Eggs of the brood-parasitic cuckoos and their hosts. In each egg pair, the egg of the host bird is shown to the left of the (usually larger) cuckoo's egg. Each of the areas separated by grey lines represents a different cuckoo species. Left upper box: European cuckoo, *Cuculus c. canorus* L. with eggs of the reed-warbler *Acrocephalus arundinaceus* (top left), with eggs of the blue-headed wagtail *Motacilla flava* (top right), with eggs of the red-backed shrike *Lanius collurio* (bottom left), with eggs of the redstart *Phoenicurus phoenicurus* (bottom right). Right upper box: Japanese cuckoo *Cuculus canorus telephonus* Heine with eggs of the Japanese red-

eared bunting *Emberizia cioides ciopsis*. Right middle box: the small Indian cuckoo *Cuculus p. poliocephalus* Lath. with eggs of the yellow-breasted prinia *Prinia flaviventris*. Bottom box: the South African cuckoo *Chrysococcyx caprius* Boddaert with eggs of *Euplectes orix turgidus* in the Transvaal (left), *Ploceus velatus nigrifrons* in the Transvaal (middle) and *P. velatus nigrifrons* in Natal (right). *Chrysococcyx caprius* thus has different eggs in the Transvaal, according to the host which is parasitised. It also lays different eggs with the same host species, depending on the location of the latter.

species. Many experiments have been carried out on this feature. In fact, most experimenters have made use of a characteristic bird behaviour pattern – the rolling of eggs back into the nest. If an egg is removed from the nest of a gull, goose, or pigeon and placed nearby, the bird soon rises and stretches out its head towards the egg, hooks its beak over the egg and rolls it back into the nest. This egg-rolling pattern can be easily and reliably elicited and is therefore ideally suited for experiments, although it is of course restricted to ground-living birds which may naturally find their eggs dislodged from the flat nest. Tree-nesting birds with cup-shaped nests and hole-nesting birds do not show this reaction because they have no need for it. It is interesting to note that some species of birds which have recently evolved from a tree-living to a ground-living habit show no egg-rolling behaviour. Conversely, secondary tree-living types showing egg-rolling also occur.

In testing the effect of different eggs or egg-dummies, it is necessary to make certain careful measurements. The brooding bird is simultaneously presented with two different eggs and one of them is rolled into the nest first. In order to obtain reliable results and to avoid chance variation, the same experiment is repeated with the two eggs until probability calculations can be employed to determine any preference for one of the eggs. Of course, the possibility of a directional preference must be excluded since many birds tend to roll in the right-hand egg first. But once this has been recognised – an experiment with two equal eggs suffices – even this preference can be used as a standard or measurement. One can investigate how much better the left-hand egg must be before the bird acts in opposition to its tendency to the right and rolls in the left egg first.

Experiments of this kind have been carried out with many birds, the most extensive on the herring-gull by Professor Baerends and his students. Over 10,000 experiments with over 500 brooding herring-gulls were performed, and just a few of the results are presented here to give an indication of the number of features responded to by the gull. First, artificial eggs were prepared resembling the original as closely as possible but varying in size

Figure 40. Rolling eggs back into the nest when they have rolled out (shown here with a greylag goose) is a particularly suitable response for testing which characters of the egg are noticed or preferred.

from a pigeon's to an ostrich's egg. The birds regularly preferred the larger egg and even preferred a larger artificial egg to their own. The form of the egg was then varied, and cubes, cylinders, pyramids, and so on, of equal volume and with natural colour patterns were presented. The normal form was preferred to all of the abnormal shapes. The colour and spot pattern of the egg were also varied. In order to verify that the bird showed a preference to differences in colour and not in brightness, the ground-colours green, yellow, brown, blue and red were made as similar in brightness as possible and also tested against eggs in different shades of grey. In this case, too, the birds regularly selected the normal green ground-colour. The spot pattern can be varied in different ways. The bird prefers spotted eggs to uniformly-coloured eggs, groups of small spots are preferred to groups of large spots, and spots which contrast heavily with the background are preferred. These individual features can be tested one against the other so that the relative effect of the characters is established. For example, how much bigger than normal must an egg without spots be in order that it will be equal to a normal egg? In this way, it can be demonstrated that spot pattern is very important to the gull, size relatively important, ground-colour somewhat less important, and shape relatively unimportant.

In order to give an idea of the number of factors which interact in this situation, it must be added that the level of motivation for flight, brooding and other behaviour must be controlled. Birds alarmed by frightening stimuli will, for example, prefer the smaller of two eggs. In addition, birds which have too few eggs in the nest or eggs at the wrong temperature become unsettled, frequently getting up from the eggs, turning the eggs repeatedly, and preening themselves. Professor Baerends also tested the effect of heating and cooling artificial, naturally painted eggs by remote control. Even the timing of the experiments during the brooding phase affects the behaviour of the birds. It can be seen very clearly that much care and patience is required to arrive at reliable results; isolated results prove nothing. In 592 experiments, 381 herring-gulls preferred the larger of two eggs, while 181 preferred the smaller; 299 preferred the normal shape, while 152 preferred abnormal shapes. Unusual choices were due to a directional preference in 75 per cent of the cases and a further proportion originated from birds about to leave the nest temporarily.

It is important that these experiments be mentioned here, since the cuckoo carries out roughly comparable experiments with its own eggs. Although the cuckoo lays its egg in the nest of the host and not beside it, the egg must in this case be properly brooded and not merely rolled into the nest. The exact experiments described

Figure 41. Various dummy eggs are shown below which were offered to birds to elicit the egg-rolling response. The medium-sized egg is the normal size for the bird.

above were not in fact carried out on hosts of the cuckoo, but simple experiments have been carried out on so many different bird species that it is possible to assume that egg-size, egg-coloration and spot-pattern are of almost universal significance. Of course, learning processes may also play a part. Tschanz has shown that individual guillemots *Uria aalge* living in colonies on the Lofoten Islands each learn to distinguish their own eggs from those of other birds, especially from those of immediate neighbours. The eggs vary in ground-colour (blue or green, grading to off-white) and pattern, the ground-colour being more important than the spot-pattern. If the pattern of the egg is changed so slowly that the parent can keep pace in re-learning to recognise the new pattern, the preference for its own eggs remains. Of course, the guillemot does not act as a host of the cuckoo, but it does provide an example of an additional factor which has to be considered. On the other hand, it is not really necessary for the hosts of the cuckoo to learn to recognise their own eggs; it suffices if they simply remove any strange-looking egg from the clutch. This would seem to apply to at least some of the species concerned. Professor Rensch carried out some interesting experiments on this phenomenon in 1924–5. First of all, he changed the colour of one of the normal eggs in a nest, thus changing just one feature of the egg. Previous experimenters had exchanged one egg with an egg from another species, and the introduced egg consequently differed from the normal eggs in size, shape and possibly weight. In every case, the birds rejected the strange egg from the nest or abandoned the clutch completely, even when one of their own eggs had been altered in colour or spot-pattern. Rensch then went one step further, and exchanged each egg of a garden warbler immediately it was laid with an egg from a lesser whitethroat. All of these eggs were accepted by the garden warbler, but the fourth egg, which was not changed, was ejected. This experiment very clearly demonstrates, at least in the case of this garden warbler, that it is the odd egg out and not necessarily a foreign egg which is ejected. It appears that those birds which act as hosts to the cuckoo distinguish their own eggs more exactly from those of strange birds than do other species. Perhaps this is an adaptation, a kind of protective mechanism, which first appeared under the pressure of parasitism by the cuckoo. The bird which raises only its own young has a greater number of descendants than a competitor which feeds a cuckoo because it has been deceived by the cuckoo's egg. The hedge sparrow, renowned for its indifference, provides an exception. This bird will even tolerate a spotted cuckoo egg alongside its own uniformly blue-green coloured eggs.

The cuckoo lays extremely small eggs in comparison with its adult body-size. The eggs do, in fact, have a much thicker and heavier shell than the host's eggs, but the host does not notice this; after all, the young cuckoo has to break this shell itself. Most striking is the correspondence in colour and pattern between the cuckoo's egg and those of the host. Mistakes do occur now and then, with varying consequences. Many birds eject the contrasting egg from the nest, and a female cuckoo which regularly lays eggs in the wrong nests will just as regularly fail to produce offspring.

If this be due to a hereditary defect, the host will eliminate the defect as a selective agent. The majority of the host species exert a very strong selective pressure which favours cuckoos with eggs imitating those of the host exactly. This is particularly obvious with eggs bearing unusual patterns, such as those of the Japanese meadow-bunting, with its thin, winding lines. A survey of known cases has shown that of 1642 cuckoo eggs laid in the correct host nest only 8 per cent were lost, while of 298 in wrong nests 24 per cent were lost. However, this does have a boomerang effect. The more successfully a bird broods out cuckoo eggs, the more certain it will be that it will lose its own young, since they are killed off by the young cuckoo. Parasites which are too successful saw off the branch upon which they are resting, for each female cuckoo needs several nests of the same host species for her eggs. In an area containing particularly successful cuckoos, Schiermann observed that the number of reed warbler nests decreased from year to year, while the percentage of nests parasitised by cuckoos increased from year to year. This means that a too well adapted cuckoo kills off its own hosts, while a poorly adapted cuckoo kills off its own offspring. Presumably, selection in both directions produces a continual oscillation in the densities of hosts and cuckoos. This effect has been demonstrated for other parasite-host relationships, but no exact experiments have yet been carried out on the cuckoo.

It is easy to imagine that a cuckoo which lays its eggs in any available nest and leaves it to chance whether its eggs are adapted to those of its host would have little probability of producing offspring. Since cuckoo eggs in the great majority of cases resemble the host's eggs, the behaviour of the cuckoo must be the active factor responsible. It is already known that a particular female cuckoo will lay the same type of egg throughout her life. This means that her eggs are pre-determined for a particular host species: of 61 eggs laid by one and the same female within 4 years, 58 were laid in the nests of meadow pipits. It also occurs that the host species has differently coloured eggs in different regions, as does the masked weaver *Ploceus velatus nigrifrons* in the Transvaal and in Natal.

In this case, the cuckoo parasitic on the weaver exhibits an amazing correspondence in the regional variation in egg coloration (figure 39). Yet the female cuckoo does not first lay an egg, examine it, and then look for a suitable song-bird clutch. It has been observed that the female cuckoo shows interest in a nest-building pair of a suitable host species and frequently visits the pair even before egg-laying begins. The cuckoo must therefore recognise its hosts, which is not so surprising since it grew up in their company!

This, however, poses a further problem. The evidence indicates that the egg pattern of each cuckoo is genetically determined. Every female cuckoo which has been raised by a particular species must have hatched from an egg whose pattern was found to be acceptable to the foster-parents. If this female later lays its eggs in the nests of the same species, then everything should fit, except for the fact that the hereditary factors of the male must also be taken into account. This leaves two possibilities. The most complex explanation would be that the hereditary factors of the male play a part in determining the egg-pattern. In this case, only cuckoos which grew up with the same host species and thus had the same egg-pattern would be able to form successful breeding pairs, with complementing hereditary factors to control the egg-pattern of the offspring; any mixture of different patterns would have fatal consequences. But how can an adult cuckoo recognise a suitable mate, and identify the foster-parentage of the prospective mate? In any case, this would mean that cuckoos with different egg-types would be genetically separate species, with no inter-breeding. Present knowledge of the mechanism of speciation indicates that such species would have been isolated from one another at some previous stage, whereas the different species can now be found together in the same areas. Apart from this, there are cuckoo races which can be separated on morphological grounds, and these do not correspond to the different egg-type groups. Female cuckoos have fairly small territories (37 to 173 acres), while the territories of the males are larger. In addition, there is no stable pair-formation. This all speaks against the first possibility. The hereditary factors of the male no doubt play a role in the normal race-formation of the cuckoo, but not in the determination of egg-types. This means that the colour and spot-pattern of the egg is possibly determined solely by the hereditary factors of the female, that is, the hereditary factor involved should be located on the female sex-chromosome. This is only an assumption for which proof is difficult to provide, since it has so far been impossible to breed European cuckoos in captivity.

The fact that the female cuckoo usually lays her eggs in nests of the correct host is probably not determined genetically, but is more likely due to a learning process taking place during the nestling phase while the female was being reared by the foster species. That eggs may be laid in the wrong nest need not indicate a bad memory. All bird species have a fairly tightly restricted breeding season, and it is possible for a cuckoo to accommodate her eggs with the host only during this period. If the breeding season of the cuckoo is longer, then a substitute host must be found for the first or last eggs to be laid.

The evolution of brood-parasitism in the cuckoo Although nobody has been able to observe the evolution of brood-parasitism in the cuckoo, it is possible to reconstruct the process of specialisation that has slowly taken place over millions of years. First of all, it is certain that the exploitation of foster-parents is a secondary phenomenon, derived from the normal breeding patterns of birds. There are cuckoos which brood themselves, and these have large eggs corresponding to their body-size. The eggs of the common cuckoo measure approximately 23 mm × 17 mm, while the eggs of the smaller, non-parasitic American cuckoo *Coccyzus americanus* are 30 mm × 23 mm in size. Cuckoos such as the great spotted cuckoo *Clamator glandarius*, which lay their eggs in the nests of large species (crows, magpies), have eggs as large as those of the Americ-can cuckoo. The first parasitic cuckoos probably exploited larger birds, and so the small eggs of many present-day cuckoos may be regarded as an adaptation to small host species. Many host birds would, in fact, probably readily accept larger eggs, but for the cuckoo it is not only important that the egg is accepted by the host; the host must be big enough to warm and brood the egg. Neither the non-parasitic cuckoos nor those parasitising large birds throw out their stepbrothers and stepsisters as nestlings, and this is another recent adaptation to small host species. Non-parasitic cuckoos have uniformly-coloured, sometimes even white, eggs, and so the eggs of parasitic cuckoos have also become more colourful as part of the specialisation towards brood-parasitism.

With the South American cuckoos of the sub-family Crotophaginae, several females together often lay up to 20 eggs in one communally-brooded clutch. The North American cuckoos of the sub-family Coccyzinae usually brood their own eggs, although sometimes they lay their eggs in the nest of a conspecific and may or may not help the pair concerned with the job of brooding the young. Occasionally, they lay their eggs in the nests of other species of bird, but these eggs never hatch. It seems that brood-parasitism has gradually evolved in this way. Sometimes, several females of the great spotted cuckoo lay eggs in the nest of the same host, such as a magpie. Each female compensates by removing one of the host's eggs (spotted, with blue-green ground-colour) from the nest and, strangely enough, the egg of another cuckoo is never removed. Presumably, the cuckoo recognises small differences between the eggs which are not noticed by the host. Yet this cuckoo, more than all others, has eggs which particularly resemble those of the host.

It appears that cuckoos were originally parasitic on one particular host species. The division of the European common cuckoo into females with different host-bonds would appear to represent a higher level of specialisation. The variously specialised cuckoo gentes no longer compete with one another for hosts, even when they occur together in the same region.

Widow-birds

Brood parasitism is found in a number of bird families. The black-headed duck *Heteronetta atricapilla* (family Anatidae) lays its eggs in the nests of other ducks, while the cuckoo finch (a weaver bird, family Ploceidae) parasitieses relatives of the warblers. Honey guides (Indicatoridae) leave their young to be reared by barbets, woodpeckers and other birds. A number of blackbirds of the family Icteridae are brood parasites of American song-birds. The widow-birds (Viduinae), which also belong to the family Ploceidae, present a particularly interesting case of mimicry.

It has already been mentioned that the young of the cuckoo exhibit sign stimuli with a very strong effect upon the fostering adult birds. Since the cuckoo disposes of its step-brothers and step-sisters, the problem of comparison by the parents, which is so important in the case of the eggs, does not arise. In the case of the great spotted cuckoo, however, the young cuckoo grows up together with the young of the foster parents, and this allows the hosts to compare their own young with the stranger smuggled into the nest. The juvenile plumage of this young cuckoo closely resembles that of the host's offspring. This resemblance of plumage is even more drastic in the widow-birds, which parasitise different species of Estrildid finches (Estrildidae). Each widow-bird species parasitises one particular finch species, producing a pattern of parasitism in the steppe and savanna regions of Africa from the Southern border of the Sahara to the tip of the Cape. In this case the colour of the eggs is not of particular importance, since the eggs of both widow-birds and the Estrildid finches are pure white. Since the relatives of the Viduinae have spotted eggs, the conclusion can be drawn that the widow-birds have lost the spots on their eggs as an adaptation to their way of life.

As a rule, the female widow-bird does not destroy any of the host's eggs, and she lays only one egg per nest. It does, however, occur that several females select the same host nest, so that the nest may eventually contain a number of parasite eggs. Nicolai's recent observations in the wild show that widow-birds will destroy eggs and probably eat the contents in the latter situation. The female widow-bird always chooses a host egg to destroy, ignoring any eggs of her own species. In this case, as in the case of the cuckoo mentioned above, it appears that the parasite distinguishes the eggs better than the host. The eggs of the widow-bird are always bigger and more oval than those of the host.

All Estrildid finches feed their young in a characteristic way, using food predigested in the crop. This is also seen in some other birds, but these always give small quantities of food pulp at a time and remove the beak from that of the young for a short period. The Estrildid finches, on the other hand, bury the beak in the throat of the young and then pump in a large part of the crop contents without stopping. This feeding technique, unique among passerines, is the basic reason underlying the fact that it is impossible to rear young Estrildid finches with other nursing adults. It is also impossible to rear foreign young with parents of domesticated Estrildid species, even though these no longer pay much attention to the beak signals discussed below. Only widow-bird nestlings are adapted for this feeding technique. The egg-colour and the type of feeding are similar in all Estrildid species and are mirrored in all widow-bird species.

The young widow-bird does not harm its nest-companions in any way. This means that the host species suffers only slightly, and there is simply one more hungry beak to fill. But this is exactly where the problem arises. The Estrildid finches have highly specialised gape patterns, far more complex than those of the other birds mentioned previously. The begging gape presented to the parents is characterised by black spots on the palate, tongue and lower mandible. In addition, the greatly thickened outgrowths on the upper and lower mandibles carry one or two rounded papillae. which are usually white, or blue in some species. This complex pattern varies from species to species. The number and position of the spots varies; they may be lost from the tongue or the lower beak, or fuse to form arches. The host parents have an innate knowledge of the species-specific gape pattern, that is, they recognise the pattern without requiring prior experience. The parents pump food only into the right pattern and ignore any young with an incompatible pattern which are smuggled into the nest. Such young would rapidly die, and so it is easy to predict the appearance of the beaks of the young widow-birds. As expected, the nestlings of the different widow-bird species are found to possess gape patterns which are indistinguishable from those of the host's young. Figure 42 provides a good example. This correspondence is parallel to that found between the eggs of the European cuckoo and its hosts. The fact that two separate groups of birds preyed upon by different brood parasites developed highly specific recognition signals and paid particular attention to the correctness of the signals, whether egg or gape pattern, indicates the results of a defensive development in the hosts.

The Estrildid finches, however, exhibit a number of additional important signals contributing to the overall begging signal. The nestlings utter specific begging calls and rotate the head in an unusual manner while begging. Both these features are copied exactly by the widow-birds. Finally, the coloration of the juvenile plumage of the parasite is identical to that of the host. Distinct differences can only be observed in the adults, as shown in figure 42. Since the young parasite in this case sits alongside the offspring of the host until leaving the nest, constantly permitting comparison, a larger number of corresponding characters is required than in the case of the young cuckoo. Just as important, but less conspicuous, are the similarities in digestive physiology. It is assumed that the young cuckoo is not particular and will just as easily allow itself to be filled up with insects by a warbler as with mouse-meat from a shrike. But it is known that the nestlings of the various widow-bird species are each dependent upon the type of food which the corresponding Estrildid species feeds to its young. Thus, the young widow-bird must be adapted in its beak markings, begging call, juvenile plumage and digestive system and this depends on which species of finch is acting as host. It is highly improbable that this is all determined by the hereditary factors of the female alone, in contrast to the cuckoo, where the Y-chromosome seems to operate to the exclusion of the male hereditary factors. Nicolai, who has carried out the most detailed investigation of brood parasitism in the widow-birds, therefore assumes that the male hereditary factors are equally important. This assumption is supported by the following findings, which demonstrate yet another amazing correspondence between host and parasite.

If it is correct that the males' hereditary factors affect the signals concerned, then a cross between widow-birds whose genetic factors determine different beak markings and so on must have fatal consequences: the hybrid will possess features which are acceptable to none of the widow-bird species and will starve. This means that only partners with similar hereditary complements determining signals important in feeding can pair successfully. But how do suitable partners recognise one another? Actually widow-birds are distinct from species to species, and so there is usually no difficulty, although this is not true of the paradise widow-bird *Steganura*. There are seven closely similar forms of this widow-bird, each of which was regarded as a separate race. But each form parasitises a separate species of Estrildid finch, and so crosses between these races must surely be prevented, that is, they must actually be separate species. But this is not the important question. What is important is the method used by these forms in distinguishing between possible partners. Individuals very similar in external appearance must each choose a partner raised by the same host, which thus bears the hereditary factors determining the correct juvenile characters. The answer to this question is surprisingly simple: recognition is based on the song of the host. Following intensive studies, Nicolai was able to show that in the males of these parasitic widow-birds only a few song elements typical of the widow-bird group occur, but that this is supplemented by many elements from the song of the right host. The males of the broad-tailed paradise widow-bird *Steganura obtusa* utter the vocalisations of the orange-winged pytrilla *Pytilia afra*, while the males of the narrow-tailed paradise widow-bird *S.paradisaea* utter the whistling strophes of the melba finch *Pytilia melba*. Both widow-birds occur together in the same area. The broad-tailed paradise widow-bird

Figure 42. The Estrildid finch *Pytilia melba* (top left) is the host of the brood-parasitic long-tailed paradise widow-bird *Steganura paradisaea* shown to the right (both are males). Beneath are 30-day old nestlings of the Estrildid finch (left) and the widow-bird (right). Since the Estrildid finches feed nestlings only in response to a species-specific gaping signal, the parasite must also imitate this. In the grey area are shown the gape patterns of one-day old nestlings of the widow-bird (left) and the Estrildid finch (right).

utters the entire vocabulary of its host and the narrow-tailed form utters only the song of the male host. The combasson *Hypochera* imitates everything that it hears in the care of its foster-parents, even the combined begging calls of a group of nest-companions crowding around an adult returning to feed. The correspondence between the songs of widow-birds and the vocalisations of the hosts is so exact that even the hosts cannot tell who is singing (figure 43).

How did this deception arise? This question remains unanswered to the present day. The young widow-birds hatching from the egg must surely be able to utter the begging call of the host young instinctively. It is improbable and unnecessary that the vocalisations of the host should be innately incorporated in the repertoire of a widow-bird since there is enough opportunity to learn these. It is a well-known fact that many juvenile birds learn the song of the male parent, even that of a male foster-parent of another species. It is therefore probable that similar learning processes are involved in the later partner selection of the widow-bird, where members of a pair have grown up with the same host species and learned the same language. This would be the first known example of a mating barrier between potentially compatible parents effected by learning.

There is still the problem, as with the cuckoo, that each female widow-bird must lay her eggs in the nests of the correct host species. Each female needs a specific male and a specific host. The female sets out to find the host, which is recognised by its song, and observes the preparation for brooding. The female synchronises with the egg-laying of the host female so that she lays her egg in the same nest at the right time. In the case of species which themselves brood the eggs, the female is stimulated by the nest-building activity of the male to mating *and* egg-laying. In this normal situation, the nest-building male is also the partner in copulation. whereas these two activities are performed by two different males where the female widow-bird is concerned. She is tuned in by the male of one species, who resembles her foster-father, while she is mounted by an innately-recognised male of her own species who resembles her true father.

Figure 43. The paradise widow-birds employ the vocalisations of the host which reared them for mutual communication. Top: segment of a recording of the song of the Estrildid *Pytilia melba*. Bottom: the same segment from the mimetic song of the paradise widow-bird *Steganura paradisaea*.

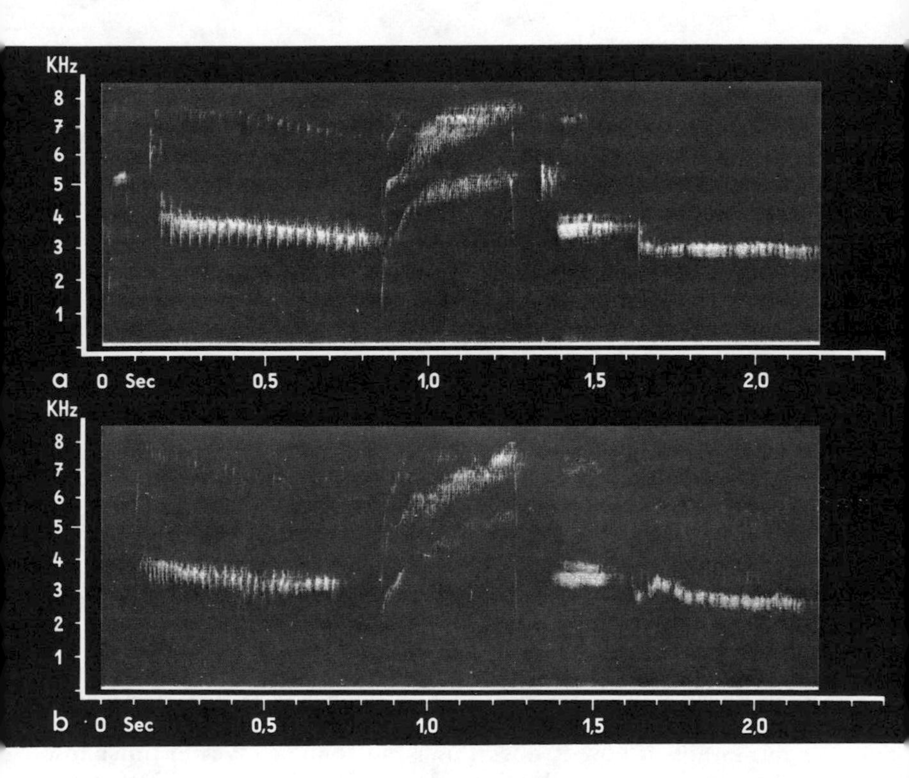

The close similarity between the gape markings of the young of the widow-birds and those of the Estrildid finches and the correspondence in the courtship calls of the adults was for a long time taken as evidence of a genetic relationship between the two groups, and widow-birds were regarded as close relatives of the finches. But it has now been shown that these characters of the widow-bird, just as with the egg-patterns of our cuckoo, happen to be subjected to a very strong selective pressure. They have attained their present form by adapting to the host.

Glow-worms as sirens

During warm summer nights it is sometimes possible to find luminous beetles of the family Lampyridae, called glow-worms. Only the males look like beetles, and the females are little different from the larvae. Glow-worms are grey during the day and the females in particular are inconspicuous, but at night, various parts of the body in both sexes light up with a green light. The luminous organs contain two substances called luciferin and luciferase. Together with oxygen, luciferin is converted to oxyluciferin; luciferase is an enzyme that converts oxyluciferin to the luminous end-product. Man has not yet been able to produce a cold source of light, that is, one producing little heat, with equal simplicity.

The larvae are also luminous, some even before hatching. They are luminous throughout the year, while the adult beetles are luminous during only a very restricted phase. Two species are especially common in Central Europe; the commonest is *Phausis splendidula* while *Lampyris noctiluca* is somewhat less common. The larvae of *Lampyris* are not continuously luminous and light up for a period lasting from one second to a number of minutes. The light often appears gradually, building up for about one second. Maximum brightness is maintained for a further second and the light then gradually dies out over the course of two more seconds. If a larva is touched while lighting up, it immediately switches off its light, although how it does this is not known. We do not know what part is played by luminescence in the life of the larva, for it is used neither to deter predators nor to attract prey. *Phausis* larvae usually light up only in response to touch or other mechanical stimuli. They usually light up for longer periods, but they can also switch the light on and off at will. Both larvae and adults only luminesce at night and never during the daytime, when they could not be seen.

Tropical species are conspicuous in that the light is usually flashed and differs in colour from species to species. Professor Hassenstein discovered in Argentina a luminous beetle, surprisingly belonging to the click beetle (family Elateridae) with two large theoracic luminous spots. These spots emit a greenish light while the beetles sit still. In flight the abdomen is bent slightly upwards and a luminous organ on the ventral surface becomes visible, which emits a yellow-red light. As long as the beetle is airborne and displaying its flying light, the 'parking lights' remain switched off. What function does this all have?

Luminescence is very important to the adults since it helps to bring the sexes together. The luminous females squat on the ground, on stones or on blades of grass, while the males fly around in search of them. This had long been postulated from observations, but the first experiments were carried out only a few years ago. Schwalb studied glow-worms and discovered that the female's light is the only signal which summons the males from afar. Olfactory substances function only at close quarters. Both *Phausis* and *Lampyris* produce light of the same wavelength (500–650 mμ, maximum transmission at 550–580 mμ) and of the same intensity. Schwalb carried out experiments with models in oder to identify the operative factors in the light signal. He used perforation patterns illuminated from beneath with light of different colours.

Lampyris shows practically no reaction towards blue, green or red light, but responds to yellow light, and the best reaction is given to light with a wavelength of about 570 mμ. There is also a favoured light intensity, corresponding to that normally produced by the female; brighter and dimmer lights are not attractive. If the models are enlarged or reduced in size, the males again respond less vigorously than to the correctly proportioned dummy female. If the model is made to blink ($\frac{1}{2}$ second light; $\frac{1}{2}$ second dark), the males then react less actively than towards a continuous light. The males also show a poorer reaction when the normal pattern of light spots is altered, even if the optimum light conditions are maintained. The results of similar experiments with *Phausis* males are entirely different. The males react to blue light, which does not occur in the light produced by the species, just as well as to the normal female light. In addition, they prefer the brightest lights and the biggest

Figure 44. Light patterns produced by two glow-worms, *Lampyris noctiluca* on the left and *Phausis spendidula* on the right, with three dummies tested for each beneath them. In *Lampyris*, the normal dummy (far left) is much more effective than the two adjacent types. Particularly striking is the poor result produced with the dummy shown on the right, in which only the orientation of the normal elements has been altered. In *Phausis*, the normal dummy (centre) is less effective than the one on the left and better than the one on the right. Multiplication of the elements produces supernormal dummies.

models. Thus, when the elements of the light pattern of the *Phausis* female are schematised, exaggerated and displayed with blue light, a supranormal model better than a real female is produced. Pure yellow light displayed through the normal spot pattern of the female also functions better than a real female. Both species occur together in Europe. As can be expected from the experimental results, *Lampyris* males easily distinguish between females of the two species, whereas *Phausis* males confuse the two and notice their mistake only when they are close enough to the females to perceive their odour.

These experiments are important to an understanding of the following case, which was first observed by Lloyd in 1965, and involves a deception which has fatal consequences. As already mentioned, most tropical glow-worms flash their lights. Closely-related species often flash at different rhythms. One species transmits once every three or four seconds, producing two flashes half a second apart, as if signalling an 'i' in Morse. Another species transmits continuous light flashes lasting a quarter of a second, alternating with quarter second pauses. In many cases, both sexes of a species flash in different ways. The male of *Phractomena lucifera* transmits five flashes in quick succession within the space of a second, while the female transmits a flash lasting one second, which slowly waxes and wanes. The males of *Photinus pennsylvanicus* transmit three rapid flashes of decreasing intensity within three quarters of a second and the females reply with a pulsating light signal, containing about eight pulses of increasing intensity emitted during an interval of one second. It will be noticed that I used the word 'reply'. The females of these species usually wait until seeing a signal from an airborne male of the same species and then signal a reply. The male then approaches with lights flashing and eventually alights beside the female. In *Photinus consanguineus* the males fly about, flashing two short light signals at intervals of

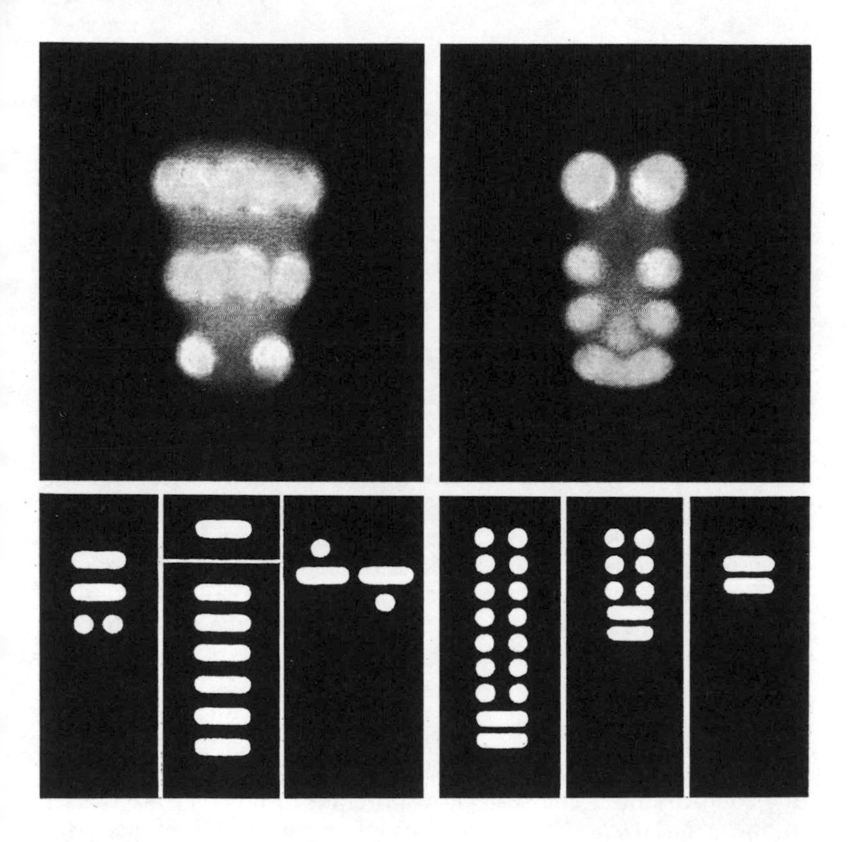

approximately two seconds. This signal is repeated once every four to seven seconds. The females reply after the second light flash of the male with a single flash of light lasting about one second.

Another genus, *Photuris*, also closely related to our native glow-worm, possesses other flashing signals for bringing the sexes together. The females are unusual in that they still continue to eat as adults, and prey upon beetles. In fact, their diet consists of the males of *Photinus* just mentioned. These males are attracted by *Photuris* females which respond to the flashing signal of male *Photuris sanguineus* with the same signal as the true females. The predatory female admittedly makes an occasional mistake of transmitting the signal after both of the male's flashes instead of after the second flash, but the males do not pay much attention to detail. They thus resemble our common glow-worms in responding to signals other than those typical of the species. The males approach and the *Photuris* female continues to transmit, even cutting down the light intensity. This is important, since the light flashes of the true female are noticeably weaker. The foreign male eventually lands alongside the wrong female. After a short exchange of flashes, the male is seized and eaten. So the predatory *Photuris* female is able to perform at least one extra signal code in addition to that typical of her own species. It is not yet known how this behaviour evolved, but the female *Photuris* provides a delightful illustration of the ancient Greek myth of the seductive Sirens. The whole story was discovered because collectors hit upon the idea of signalling with a torch for the females of a particular species of beetle which they were hunting. The females answered back, but sometimes with the result that the wrong females were found.

Attractive orchids

A number of orchids are pollinated by insects without providing any compensation. The best-known orchids of this type are species of the genus *Ophrys*. The beautiful flowers of this orchis have attracted the attention of human beings for centuries, giving rise to an imaginative nomenclature: *Ophrys insectifera*, *O.muscifera*, *O.aranifera*, *O.apifera*, *O.bombiflora*, or fly-orchis, humming-bee orchis, spider-orchis, bee-orchis. These names all refer to the form and coloration of the flower, more precisely to the labellum. In 1745, Linnaeus recorded that the flowers of *Ophrys insectifera* so closely resemble flies that the uninitiated would believe that the stem were actually occupied by squatting flies, since even artists could not have imitated flies with greater effect. It was assumed that this similarity was not a caprice of nature, but must have some biological function. But what is this function? Flowers regularly act as signals for insects which carry out pollination, and so much thought was given to the manner in which these orchids might attract insects. It was assumed quite early on that the insects see

Figure 45. The flowers of some orchid species are highly specialised dummy females for males of certain species of bee and wasp, which pollinate the flowers in an attempt to copulate with them. The flower of the bee orchis *Ophrys apifera* looks to the human observer extremely like a hovering bee or bumble-bee.

these flowers just as we do and take them for conspecifics. In addition, it was assumed that potential visitors of a flower would fly past if any flower were already occupied. But why should orchids deter insects instead of attracting them? Admittedly, many orchids are self-fertilised and Brown expressed the opinion in 1831 that *Ophrys* species scared off insects with their flowers, since their aid was not required. But since these orchids do not have nectar in any case, it was not easy to see why they should go to such lengths to deter insects. The source of theoretical wisdom dried up.

The solution to the problem could have been easily found through observation. When observers investigated orchids later they noticed only male insects on the flowers and agreed in the interpretation that insects treated the flowers like mating partners and consequently pollinated them. In fact, nobody had observed any other form of pollination in these flowers. Nevertheless, the experts did not accept this interpretation and doubted the reliability of the observations. But an increasing number of observers reported the same phenomenon and in 1961, Professor Kullenberg conducted investigations in the field and filled an entire volume of a journal with his results. The pollination of *Ophrys* flowers and those of related species is actually carried out by copulation with male insects, though the insects deliver pollen for fertilisation and not insect sperm. The male insects carry the entire pollen sacs and anther stem from one flower to the next in a very simple manner.

Many of the barbed Hymenoptera have an excess of males, which fly around in search of receptive females. Many species fly along special paths which are continually used in these searching flights. As in the case of many butterflies, form, colour and odour all play a part in recognition. Many species can be provoked to make a trial landing on female-like objects without difficulty, but for copulation, tactile stimuli play an important role. The main visitors of Ophrys *flowers* are males of the mining bee *Andrena* and the horned bee *Eucera*, the digger-wasps (Sphecidae) and the dagger-wasps (Scoliidae). The Australian orchis *Cryptostylis* is visited by male ichneumons (Ichneumonidae) of the genus *Lissopimpla*.

Observations show that these males activate their genital appendages on the flower and that in many cases the copulatory organ touches the labellum of the flower or may even be extruded. Nobody (not even Kullenberg) has found ejaculate on the flower. While the males carry out introductory courtship and mating movements on the flower, the pollen sacs become attached to the insect's body and are carried to the next flower when the male flies further on. All observations lead to the inevitable conclusion that *Ophrys* flowers have the effect of female dummies on the male insects. As would logically be expected, the individual *Ophrys* species are each specialised for a particular insect species, that is, each mimics the corresponding female. There are nevertheless overlap effects, so that the same males may sometimes visit different *Ophrys* species and thus effect cross-pollination. It is not my intention to deal with the many interesting details of this phenomenon, but rather to give a general survey of Kullenberg's investigations. The interesting features are the important characteristics of the flower involved in this pseudocopulation, and these will be illustrated with the example of the fly-orchis *O.insectifera*, which is visited mainly by *Gorytes* males (Sphecidae). The important thing to be borne in mind is the distinction between the male's reactions before and after landing on the flower.

The first important feature in an efficient female dummy is its size. Flowers which are too small are visited by males, but are then abandoned. Males also alight on over-large flowers, which occasionally occur, and they then press backwards with the abdomen applied to the labellum until they come to the edge of the two terminal lobes, which are distinctly papillated. At the edge, the insects probe about with the tip of the abdomen and the associated copulatory apparatus. From this, it can be clearly seen that the males are not heading for possible food material in the inside of the flower, but are seeking some specific feature with the genitalia. Over-large flowers are disadvantageous for the plant since the head of the male does not reach up to the stigma to transfer the pollen.

The form of the labellum does not play a very large part, although elongated oval objects are more attractive to the male than quadratic shapes. The males fly up to a wide range of objects; they even approach living bees in the wild and many simple dummies are approached in experiments. Wasp-like shapes are more attractive than other forms and movement of the object works better than immobility. The best sign stimuli were the labellum of *Ophrys insectifera* and the folded wings of a *Gorytes* wasp on a dark background, provided that they were presented together with olfactory stimuli. It appears that particular odours stimulate the males to fly up to practically anything, be it the head of a nail or a dark spot on a leaf.

The coloration of the labellum is an important factor in the approach of the male. The males prefer dark colours to light and will react to darker shades of grey. Blue and violet produce the best response, and if they contain a significant ultra-violet component they will function even better than actual females. A contrast spot in the middle of the dummy increases its effectiveness, and the same effect can be achieved by adding a small piece of glass or engineering a metallic sheen. A velvety surface works better than a smooth one. It does not require much imagination to draw a connection between the signal of the *Ophrys* flower shown to be most effective to the Hymenopteran male and the female of the Hymenopteran species concerned. In some cases, it has even been possible to deduce from the flowers important indications of the actual copulatory behaviour of such insects. But in order to avoid too much theorising Kullenberg also included the females of the *Ophrys*-visitors in his investigation. The centre of the labellum of *Ophrys insectifera* bears a dark red spot, which appears almost black, whereas the lateral lobes are a somewhat lighter shade of purple-red. The *Gorytes* females, whose males are so attentive towards these flowers, are black dorsally and bear dark purple wings. The abdomen bears yellow or white cross-stripes, but these are lacking in the flower. When the females fold their wings together over the abdomen, a glistening area is produced which closely resembles the shiny spot on the labellum of the flower. It is legitimate to compare the dorsal view of the female with the flower, since this is naturally the side which the male approaches. When the characters so far investigated are compared, some are seen to be additive, though all are to some extent independent, and some can replace each other. An additional factor is movement, which is produced in the flower by wind.

Odour plays a particular role in attracting the male. Some female Hymenoptera secrete odiferous substances which sexually arouse males and make them attentive to females. The odour causes the males to search for females, and in the course of the search, they approach objects which have little in common with a real female. These odours may be species-specific and they certainly function only within a particular group of species, so that mistakes are possible within a limited range. These odiferous substances have not yet been chemically analysed, although the structure of similar attractants of some species has recently been elucidated. But it is possible for us to determine differences between these substances with our own powers of smell and to identify chemical substances which to us appear to smell similar to a given female scent. Kullenberg tested substances of this kind in the wild in combination with dummy females of very different types while testing male Hymenoptera which visit *Ophrya* flowers. He found a number of substances which could be relied upon to attract the males. But this is not the most interesting fact: he found that the *Ophrys* flowers also give off an odour, an odour which is very similar to, if not identical with, that produced by the female of the insect species. In some cases, the odour of the flower is actually more effective than that of the female in attracting the male. These orchids therefore imitate the sexual attractant odour of certain insect species and even represent supranormal chemical dummies. As soon as we know more about the sexual attractants of these insects, it will be one of the most fascinating tasks of chemical physiologists to determine how these plants copy the odours of the insects.

Figure 46. Below: how male insects react to the female-like flowers of orchids. Top left: flower of the fly orchis *Ophrys insectifera*. Bottom: male of the long-horned bee attempting to copulate with the flower, with the head of the bee with attached pollen sacs shown top right. Right: flower of the Australian *Cryptostylis leptochila* with males of the wasp *Lissopimpla semipunctata*. In the middle, the male attempts to copulate with the flower. The pollen sacs are shown on the abdomen (bottom). P = pollen sacs (pollinia).

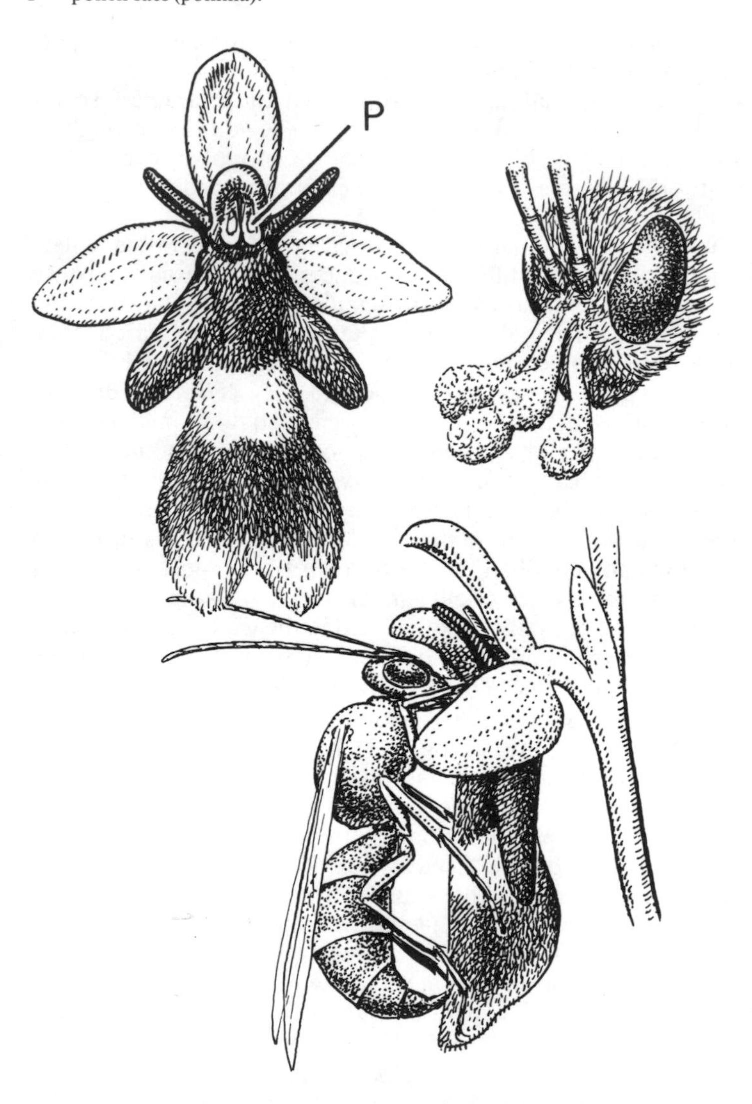

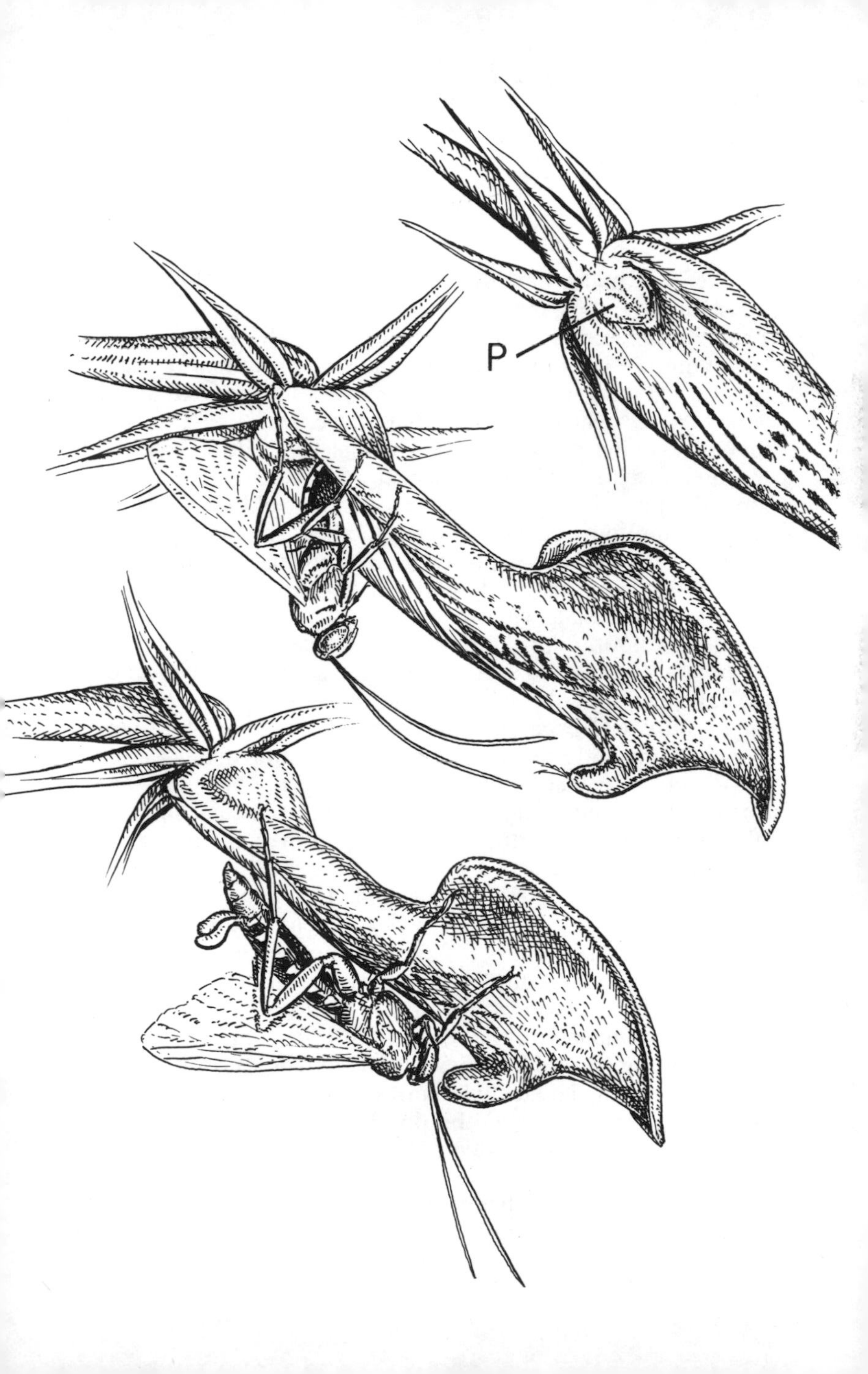
P

When the males have landed upon an *Ophrys* flower or some other dummy, they begin to show introductory mating behaviour. This requires further signal stimuli, above all tactile stimuli. The labellum must be convex dorsally, just like the dorsal surface of the females. Males will indeed land upon old, shrivelled flowers or young flowers which do not yet have the convex dorsal surface, but they immediately fly off again. The males will do little more than this on an isolated labellum, since the counterpressure on the head normally provided by the smaller petals is lacking. The surface of the labellum must be wide enough to allow the male to press with its lower surface, particularly the abdomen. The tactile stimuli perceived by the underside and legs of the male are particularly important. The male will not attempt proper copulation on smooth paper, nor upon a labellum which has been artificially smoothed. In these two cases, the decisive long and short hairs typical of both the labellum and the back of the female are lacking. It is not important what appearance the hairs have, as long as the flexibility is right. Long and short hairs must occupy quite distinct areas, and the direction in which they are inclined probably plays an additional role. It must once again be emphasised that all these sign stimuli only exert an attractive effect upon the male in the presence of the female odour.

If the behaviour of the various male Hymenoptera is compared with that of the orchis flowers to which each is adapted, it becomes apparent that there are two types of flowers. On some, the males always sit with the head directed towards the centre of the flower, while on others the males sit facing in the opposite direction. Since all males copulate with the females with the same orientation, the head pointing towards the head of the female, this means that the proximal end of the labellum corresponds to the female's anterior end in the first case and the distal end in the second. For this reason, the males carry away the pollen sacs either on the head or on the tail end (figure 46).

In the meantime, Kullenberg and others have examined a whole series of orchis species all of which are pollinated by insects. This specialisation has meant that each orchis is dependent upon a restricted number of pollen transporters, since only males of definite species are aroused by the dummy females in each case. This places a restriction on the distribution of the orchids since they are fertilised only in those regions where 'their' males occur. The bee-orchis *Ophrys apifera* is pollinated by males of the horned bee in the Mediterrancan arca, but it is also particularly well adapted for self-pollination. For this reason, this orchis was able to penetrate up the Rhône valley in the warm period following the Ice Ages and is almost entirely dependent upon self-pollination in the new settlement areas.

Once again, we are confronted with the question of the identity of the substances in the flowers which resemble the sexual attractant odours and the manner in which they were developed. It is actually not so very difficult for the plant to develop such substances, and it is even possible that the question should be reversed. If plants and animals are compared, it is found that plants are characterised by an unusually large number of waste synthesised substances, in some cases very complex, which do not play a part in growth and are stored in the plant. Such substances include alkaloids, terpenes, phenylpropanes, resins, lignanes and lignins, saponins, flavonoles, anthocyanes, and so on. These are referred to as metabolic waste-products or secondary metabolites of plants, although this description is ill-fitted, as Professor Mothes recently emphasised. Such substances are frequently encountered because plants do not have the excretory systems necessary to eliminate them. The same substances also occur in the animal kingdom, particularly when the animals concerned cannot discharge such substances from the body, at least for a period of time. This is the case, for example, with the developing eggs of insects, most reptiles, and birds, and with insect pupae. The secondary plant metabolites are not taken up as such by the animals concerned, they are produced within the animal, sometimes in the same way as in plants. Some of the substances of this type represent metabolic poisons, and are discharged by the highly developed excretory systems of animals, often in a harmless form in the urine. But some of the excretory materials of animals comparable with the secondary plant metabolites are stored in glandular pockets, as in toads, salamanders, and insects, or in musk-glands, as in the beaver and, muskrat. The arthropods, including the insects, are especially notable for the production of typical plant excretory substances and they often employ them as defensive substances. Glomerid millipedes (Glomeridae, often confused with centipedes by the uninitiated) secrete a bitter quinazolone which repels birds. Quinazolones differing only in the absence of one side-group are also found in species of ivy (Araliaceae), saxifrages (Saxifragaceae), rues (Rutaceae) and in palms. We do not yet know how these substances are kept inactive in the animals, and we have no idea how they are produced. But we cannot conclude that the occasional restriction to a specific function for given chemical substances – such as sexual attractants – must necessarily have been laboriously evolved for the purpose concerned. It may be that nature follows the easy way and simply makes use of substances which are present in any case. This would mean that the imitation of such substances by other organisms would be less surprising than at present appears to be the case.

Beetles, characins and wedding gifts

It is said that the way to a man's heart is through his stomach. The same thing often applies to animals. Many birds feed each other during courtship, in particular parrots, doves, and members of the raven family (Corvidae). The feeding behaviour is derived from parental care behaviour and this secondarily derived function may be retained when the actual parental behaviour is lost, as is the case with some cuckoos. In some cases, a social bonding pattern emerges from such behaviour, for example in the wood swallow *Artamus*, in colonial insects (termites, ants, bees, wasps) and in the hunting dog *Lycaon*. Reciprocal feeding as a greeting pattern can eventually be reduced to a pure gesture. The social significance is retained, but food is not longer provided. This is seen in ravens, hunting dogs, wood swallows and chimpanzees. In these cases, the source of the behaviour can easily be recognised as being a rudiment remaining after the reduction of a true feeding pattern. This is not to be described as an imitation of true feeding, since the only difference shown is the secondary loss of food-provision.

Various male spiders present the female of the species with a wrapped-up package of prey in order to occupy her attention during copulation. This would seem to be distracting behaviour since female spiders can be a definite threat to their own males. Similar presents are offered by the males of predatory robber-flies (Empididae). Here, the females do not normally prey upon living organisms, but the males bring a trapped, immobilised insect before mating. *Empis* species do not wrap up the prey, but some other genera spin a wrapper with a secretion from glands located on the fore-legs. Other male species bring dummy presents when courting the female, offering an attractively spun package containing nothing at all. This behaviour is derived from genuine present-giving by the evolution, through gradual stages, of the predominance of packaging over the inclusion of a gift of food.

Dummy objects of this kind with a similar function also occur in other animal groups, particularly among certain groups of insects. Attractant or stimulant food offerings play a great part in bringing the two sexes together. Hermaphrodite slugs (*Arion*) eat a mucous secretion produced by the partner before copulation, and this increases sexual arousal. Various male flies feed their females. *Rivellia* and *Cardicephala* feed the females with regurgitated droplets of liquid food; the scorpion flies (*Panorpa* species) deposit small proteinaceous balls formed from solidified saliva in front of the female, although the male does not produce these pellets if the female is willing to copulate without them.

In all the examples so far mentioned, the females are provided with food, food-wrappings, or droplets of saliva, that is, with food that the male could also consume. Sometimes, however, the males exude secretions from particular areas of the body; the secretions are inaccessible for the male and are only eaten by the female. Such secretions have not yet been investigated, although they are probably produced by special glands and are thus different from the normal food passed on by the males. Examples of this phenomenon are found in large numbers among the Orthoptera (grasshoppers, cockroaches, roaches, etc.). The males of the hothouse grasshopper *Tachycines asynamorus*, cave crickets of the genus *Troglophilus* and other Orthoptera (*Pristocentophilus*, *Isophya*) bear abdominal appendages or pockets which produce a glandular secretion for the benefit of the females. It must, of course, be added that the female sits on the male during copulation, and this enables the male to insert a spermatophore into the female's genital aperture. It is not yet known whether the secretions induce the female to climb on to the male's back, to keep her still during copulation, or both. Corresponding glands in the males of several genera of roaches (*Blatella*, *Supella*, *Ectobius*, *Parcoblatta*) are offered to the female for licking before copulation, which enables the male to lure the female into a position which permits him to grasp her genitalia with his genital appendages.

The most extensive investigation into the structure and function of such secretory organs was carried out by Matthes on Malachiid beetles. Male beetles of the family Malachiidae possess deep impressions or folds on the tips of the elytra, which bear various membraneous, leathery or horny outgrowths in the form of spines, bulbs or angular processes. Some species also bear similar processes on the forehead, antennae, or palps. There are also differences in courtship within the group, although all these beetles exhibit the same overall pattern of presenting the secretory organs to the female. If the female is receptive, she assumes the copulatory posture after partaking of the secretion, allowing the male to climb on her and copulate. The secretion seems to have a stimulating effect on the female and elicits specific mating behaviour patterns. It is therefore impossible to maintain that the female is deceived, although there is no explanation for the initial stimulation of the female to imbibe the secretion.

Figure 47. Courtship of the swordtail characin *Corynopoma riisei*, in which the male holds out the appendage of the gill operculum to the female as a dummy prey. The male of the related *Pterobrycon landoni* (bottom) develops a corresponding process from a scale.

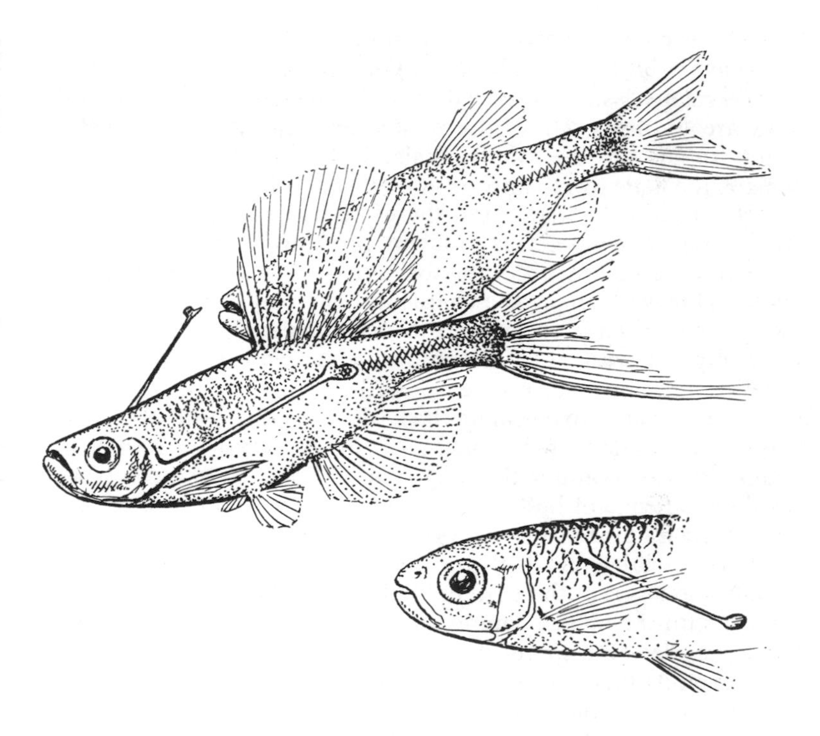

These examples illustrate the difficulty of differentiating between feeding, pseudo-feeding, attraction of the partner with a scent, and the delivery of signal materials, which are in all likelihood camouflaged as food. If the secretion of the male did not attract the female, she would not eat it. Since eating or biting patterns are elicited, the secretion must bear a similarity to normal food, even though it contains no nutrient substances and thus deceives the female. We shall return to this problem later.

A very clear instance of deception exists in the male swordtail characin *Corynopoma riisei*. This well-known ornamental fish is an inhabitant of Venezuelan rivers and belongs to the large family of characins (Characidae; sub-family Glandulocaudinae). This species and its relatives show a special reproductive peculiarity in that the eggs are fertilised within the female and are later deposited on plants in the absence of the male. In order to copulate with a female, the male has to approach closely at a time when the female is not yet ready to spawn and therefore will normally not tolerate males in their vicinity. This problem, presented here in a simplified, though nevertheless accurate form, has been solved in a most remarkable way among the characins. The male steadfastly courts any female which it encounters. Nelson has analysed the complex courtship behaviour of the swordtail characin down to the finest detail. This author has even employed cybernetic techniques and a computer in order to elucidate the basic feed-back systems controlling the motivation of the males. All that concerns us here is one significant observation: the male bears a long, spoon-like process on the hind edge of both gill opercula. When the male is aroused, the terminal bulbs of these processes become considerably darker. A courting male spreads the gill operculum on the side facing the female and twitches the terminal bulb to and fro. This provides the female with the illusive impression of a small prey organism, such as a water-flea. She approaches and may even bite the bulb, and the male exploits this approach for copulation. A further example of an analogous duplication of lures will be discussed later. Since corresponding structures, in this context, signal dummies, are developed in different ways by closely related forms (figure 47), it is particularly evident that this is not a freak of nature but a development of a structure to fulfil a specific function.

16 Intraspecific mimicry

There are examples where all three members of a mimicry system – model, mimic and signal-receiver – rather than just two are members of the same species. As yet, only a few such cases have been found, and a particularly fine example is discussed here.

Some of the tropical fresh-water fish of the family Cichlidae show an extraordinary form of parental care. The female takes up the eggs into her mouth after spawning. Here the eggs are well aerated by the respiratory water current and remain protected from predators until they hatch or even until the young are almost self-sufficient. This mouth-brooding habit originates from the more primitive open-brooding condition, where the parents watch over the eggs, attached to a leaf or a stone, until hatching. The freshly-hatched larvae are subsequently transferred to a prepared hollow in the substrate and guarded until they are able to swim away with the parents. About two to four days pass between spawning and hatching, and during this time the parents repeatedly probe the eggs with the mouth. Eventually, the ripe eggs are plucked off or the larvae are removed from the ruptured egg membrane.

In the course of evolution from open-brooding to mouth-brooding, the parents take the eggs into the mouth progressively earlier. The South American *Geophagus jurupari*, for some unknown reason known as the devil's angle, watches over the eggs on a stone for 24 hours and then takes them into the mouth, where they hatch two days later. Some African *Tilapia* species allow only about 10 minutes to elapse after spawning; others wait scarcely 2 minutes. *Haplochromis* species take each batch of eggs into the mouth as soon as it is laid, and the Cichlid *Tropheus* from Lake Tanganyika lays almost all of its eggs singly and immediately snaps up the individual eggs. The egg uptake starts progressively earlier in the spawning behaviour sequence. However, the eggs are primitively fertilised in the interval, initially still present in mouth-breeders, between spawning and gathering. Yet the highly specialised mouth-brooders leave no such interval for the female rapidly gathers the eggs before they have been fertilised.

The only reason why this does not have catastrophic conse-

Figure 48. In the African mouth-brooding fish *Haplochromis burtoni*, the male bears egg-dummies on the anal fin, and the female reacts to these in the same way as to genuine eggs. In the typical courtship posture (below) the male attracts the female with the dummy clutch of eggs. When fertilising the eggs (right) the male again spreads the anal fin and the female attempts to take the dummy eggs into her mouth along with the real eggs. The whole sequence is shown in figure 49.

quences is the fact that a novel method of fertilisation exists. The highly specialised mouth-brooders show a division of labour between the sexes. The male digs and guards the spawning hollow, carries out courtship, and leads the female to the hollow; the female broods the eggs and then cares for the young. The greater the division of labour between the sexes, the greater the difference in coloration. The male usually exhibits display coloration during the breeding season, and in many species this includes round, red colour spots on the dorsal, tail and anal fins. In fact, the fins are folded during spawning in substrate-brooding Cichlids, but this is due to the fact that these form stable pairs long before spawning. The partners of a pair recognise each other accurately, and spreading of the fins, which is typical of conflict situations involving semi-acquainted or totally unacquainted fish, disappears at an early

stage. However, this bond between the pair has been lost in mouth-brooders and the partners now exhibit only direct encounters lasting for a few minutes for spawning, without recognising each other. For this reason, the males, which perform the task of protecting the hollow, spread the unpaired fins even during the discharge of sperm and the colour spots are then conspicuously displayed. The females on the other hand actively search for mislaid eggs in order to take them into the mouth. In this process, they examine any object which looks like an egg, and to be helpful, the male removes as many egg-sized stones as possible when digging the hollow. The eggs of mouth-brooders are larger than those of open-brooders and contain more yolk.

One can imagine what happens when such a mouth-brooder is spawning. The female immediately takes all of the eggs into her

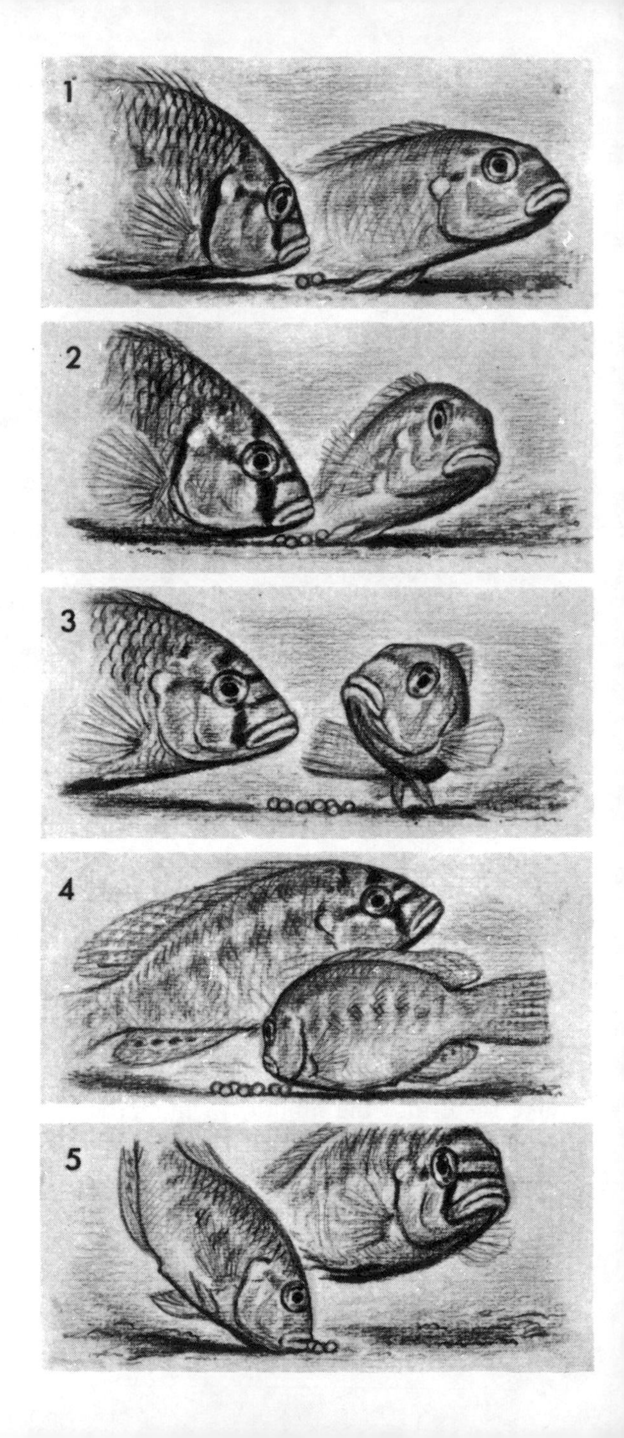
1
2
3
4
5

Figure 49. Phases in the spawning sequence in *Haplochromis burtoni*.
1–3: the female deposits a batch of eggs (female on the right).
4–5: the female collects the eggs into her mouth, where she broods them. The male waits in the background, and has not yet fertilised the eggs.
6–8: the male emits sperm on to the bare substrate while the female attempts to take up the dummy eggs into her mouth. The semen enters her mouth in the process and fertilises the eggs there.
9: the female deposits another batch of eggs.

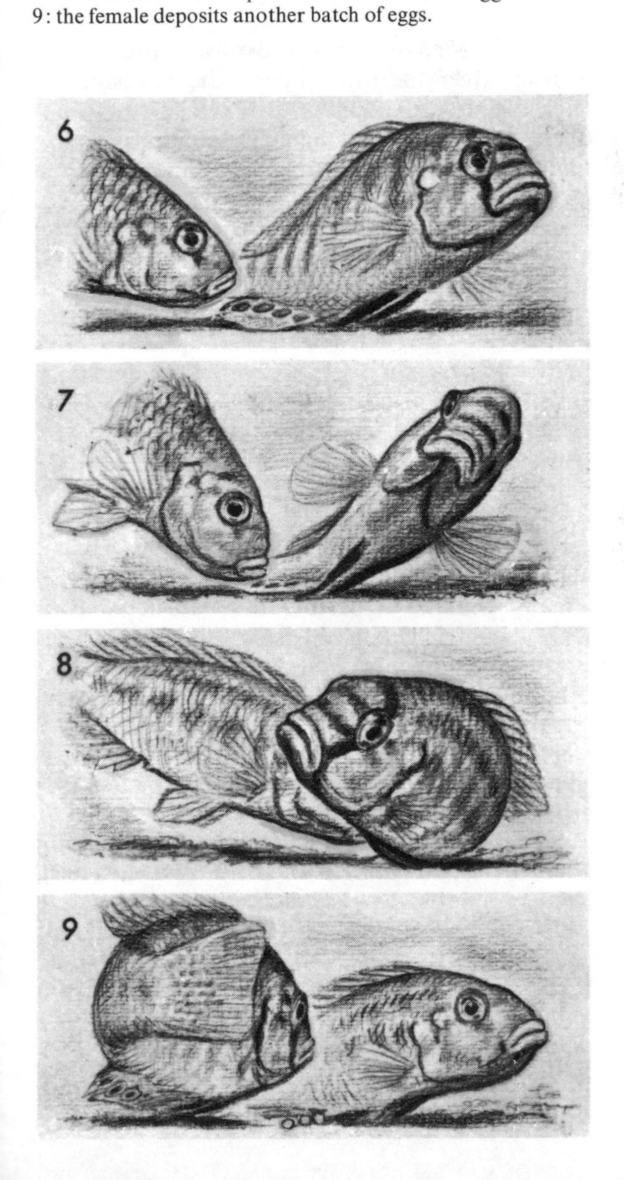

mouth, the fertilising male spreads her fins, exposing the reddish spots, the anal fin drags over the sand during the discharge of semen and the female repeatedly attempts to take the round fin-spots into her mouth as if they were eggs. Since the spots are located next to the male sexual aperture, spermatozoa automatically end up in the female's mouth.

Fortunately, we can fairly easily reconstruct the evolution of oral fertilisation by comparison with species which show various intermediate stages. The ultimate stage in this evolutionary process takes the following form. The female takes up all the unfertilised eggs, the male waits until the female has collected up all the eggs and then lies obliquely on one side, discharges sperm and spreads out the anal fin across the substrate in front of the female. The round spots on the anal fin which then appear correspond in form, colour and shape with the eggs of the particular species and the effect is enhanced by a contrasting ring. The female repeatedly attempts to take up these conspicuous egg-dummies, just as she does with individual eggs lying on the substrate. The female's gathering motions are unmistakable – she is not biting, digging or eating. Since with many Cichlids a partner that is spawning or discharging sperm may be pushed in the side with the other's mouth, the appropriate position may have been already present. The egg-dummies may be just an insurance that pushing will be converted to sucking.

The male *Haplochromis* thus mimics the eggs of its own species with his anal fin and the female responds accordingly. The fact that such deceptive signals can develop within one species is clear indication that a selective advantage is involved. An investigation of this example offers three advantages over studies of typical examples of mimicry. First, the female reacts alternately to the model (egg) and mimic (egg-dummy), with only a few seconds between repetitions. Secondly, this takes place within a spawning hollow, that is, in one place, so alterations in environmental conditions can be virtually ignored. Alterations in motivation within the reacting animals are similarly absent. Thirdly, the

Figure 50. An evolutionary series of egg-dummies on the anal fins of various African cichlid species passing from a simple spot pattern (top left) to the supernormal egg-dummy (bottom right) – as, for example, in the genus *Schubotzia*, which is related to *Haplochromis*.

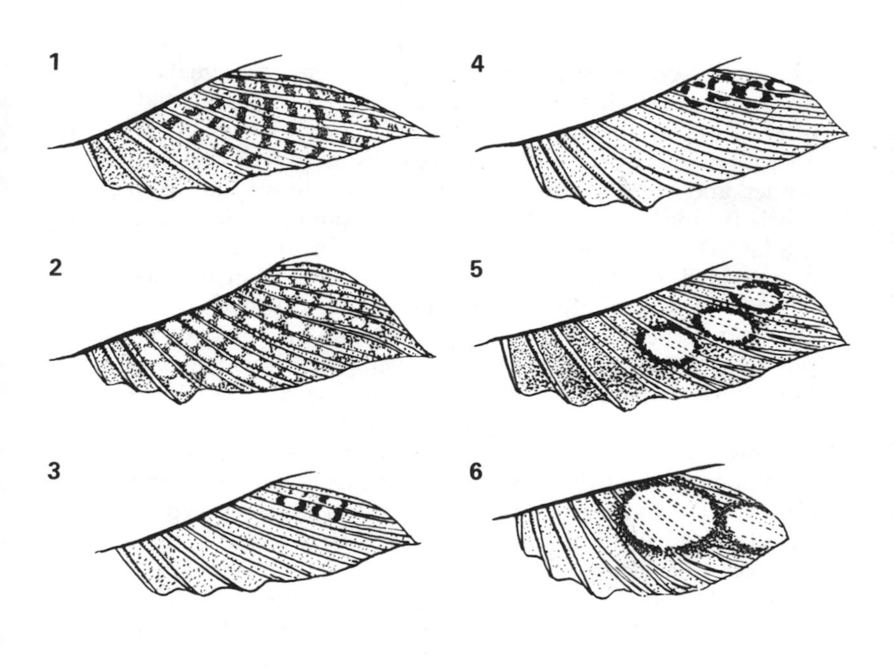

investigation of the evolution of this signal system requires the analysis only of a quite isolated group of closely related species. In more typical cases of mimicry, several or many different groups of species from quite different groups of animals must be investigated whose behavioural peculiarities and ecological relationships in the wild are only fragmentarily known. I have given the term intraspecific mimicry to this form of self-imitation (automimesis) within a species. (The question of the definition of mimicry will be dealt with in the final chapter.) Several similar cases in fish have since been demonstrated, and a further example is discussed in the next chapter.

17 Mimicry and the evolution of signals

The would-be investigator of the phylogeny of signals is in an awkward position. Signals develop only when a potential signal-receiver is available to perceive them. In other words, the development of a signal occurs only where there is an association between sender and signal-receiver. A one-sided interest can lead to the specialisation of a signal-receiver, for example, where a predator is adapted to recognise its prey as rapidly as possible, or vice-versa. A one-sided interest can also lead to the dismantling of a signal, for example, where a predator is adapted to approach its prey unnoticed or where the prey is adapted to remain as inconspicuous as possible. However, a signal is developed only when a signal-receiver shows a vested interest. Thus, the researcher who attempts to reconstruct the phylogeny of highly developed communication systems has his work cut out to determine how much of the development is attributable to the sender and how much to the receiver. The only exception where one can study the evolution of a signal in which the receiver has no vested interest is provided by mimics. For example, the wasp (model) and the bird (signal-receiver) are both interested in the black-and-yellow band signal transmitted by the wasp; the wasp does not want to be eaten and the bird does not want to be stung. However, the bird is not interested in avoiding the hover-fly, and only the latter profits.

One can take the communication system between the model and the signal-receiver as constant. Where the receiver has to learn the signal, the model can fairly easily undergo compensatory evolution under the pressure of the mimic, that is, alter its signal in order to shake off the irksome mimic. An example of this is provided by the cleaner-fish *Labroides*. The same thing appears to happen when the model and the signal-receiver belong to the same species, and once again only one species has to undergo compensatory adaptation. An example of this is provided by the Estrildid finches parasitised by widow-birds. The finches, like the cleaner-fish, show a quite unusual degree of specific variability as regards the relevant characters, an indication of extremely rapid evolution.

Any adaptation to the mimic by the signal-receiver could only result from it being able to distinguish between model and mimic, and this would result in more exact mimicry, which would make such a distinction impossible. But this means that in this case we can actually predict the future path of evolution, and mimicry thus offers researchers of evolution three great advantages. First, mimetic signals are produced by the mimic for its benefit alone, without any complementary adaptation on the part of the signal-receiver. Secondly, the ultimate stage in the evolution of a signal is already present in the form of the model. One can investigate which characters of the model have communicative value by carrying out experiments with dummies on the signal-receivers. Mimetic signals therefore incorporate evolutionary trends whose 'ultimate goal' is already known. Thirdly, we are also aware of the reaction of the receiver to the signal.

Of course, this can be demonstrated particularly well in instances of intraspecific mimicry, as with the egg-dummies of *Haplochromis*. These dummies elicit a quite specific response from the female – the taking-up of the eggs. At first, no transition takes place in this response, that is, in the intentions of the female when eggs are seen; the female attempts to take them up to brood them. However, a quite different effect is achieved – the fertilisation of the eggs. The motivation of this response is not altered, but the function changes; a brooding response becomes a fertilisation response. Even so, a further functional change does occur. As mentioned, female *Haplochromis* take up eggs as soon as they are laid. *Haplochromis* males wait by their spawning hollows until a female in spawning condition arrives. The males then swim up to the females, each attempting to lure one to his hollow. When doing this, the courting males display their coloration, including the egg-dummies (figure 48). Even at this stage the maternal instinct responds to the dummy eggs. The female approaches the egg-dummies, intending to take them into her mouth, and consequently follows the male to the hollow. Since the males with the most attractive egg-dummies have the greatest chance of success, this has led to the evolution of strongly supernormal egg-dummies. So before spawning the brooding response of the female is exploited to bring the sexes together.

If as one reverses this argument, one is provided with a very efficient method for determining the origin of social signals. Instead of predicting in which direction the mimic will evolve with the aid of observations on model and signal-receiver, one can attempt to determine the nature of the model from mimic and signal-receiver. For example, if one were to see how the *Haplochromis* females react to round, coloured spots on the anal fin of the male, without knowing why, one could produce the hypothesis that the spots are mimics of something and that they are mistaken for something by the females. This method can be called the 'search for the model'. One would determine which characters are common to all species with such spots, at the same time contrasting these with species without spots, list the situations in which the spots are conspicuously displayed, determine whether subsidiary characters of the spots correspond with some particular thing, and so on. In this way, one would find that such spots occur only in species of different genera which are mouth-brooders, that the spots are absent or very faint in the female but often occur in the male alone, that they are particularly conspicuous when the fins are spread, and that the colour and size of these spots, varying from species to species, in each case correspond to the colour and size of eggs of the species. The working hypothesis that the spots are egg-dummies could then be tested by planned observations on the act of spawning.

The following example demonstrates that such neat reconstructions are not restricted to cases where the answer is already known. Why, for example, do male hamadryas baboons have such a conspicuous red backside? Comparing male Old World monkeys, similarly coloured backsides are found in ground-living monkeys, they occur only in species in which the females show conspicuous oestrous swellings, they are presented to the partner in social greetings, and in many species they exhibit amazing similarity in form to the female genitalia. The working hypothesis that these patterns are mimics of female sexual signals can be confirmed by studies of social behaviour. Presentation of the backside with the tail raised or held aside is the typical invitation to copulation made to the male by the female. This display also inhibits aggression and is particularly important in species with large males which are socially higher in rank than the females. Large males are particularly important for ground-living species, which cannot scamper up trees when in danger. In addition, presentation is employed to appease aggressive group companions of either sex, and low-ranking males will present to high-ranking females. Presentation is also employed in a subdued form as a greeting to higher ranking members, comparable to a man taking off his hat to a superior. The strong protection this gives against attack is demonstrated by so-called secured threat, whereby one animal threatens another with angry squeals, which automatically summon the highest rank to the scene. If the threatening animal now presents to the highest ranking animal, the latter by-passes him and chases off the threatened individual, and the originator of the quarrel comes off scot-free. In species with particularly belligerent males, the females develop special colour signals to accentuate the presentation gesture during the oestrous phase, when they have to approach the high-ranking males to the point of physical contact. These signals consist of red swellings of the ano-genital region, sometimes of almost pathological appearance. Since the males also greet and subdue one another with presentation gestures they must imitate these swellings of the female if their presentation is to be as effective. In this case, the imitation has a different function from the original, for the males never employ the dummy oestrous swellings for pre-copulatory purposes, but only in a social context.

The dummy oestrous swellings also represent intraspecific mimicry. However, these examples raise the problem of the evolution of social signals. The search for the model has also helped us to find the correct interpretation in other, similar cases. This process is based upon the assumption that the signal concerned, now highly refined, has passed through a mimetic phase at which time it would

Figure 51. 'Presentation' serves both as an invitation to copulation and as a social greeting (top row). The strong inhibitory effect on attackers is demonstrated by 'secured threat' (bottom row), in which the centre animal threatens that on the left and presents at the same time to the high-ranking male on the right. The latter subsequently chases off the threatened animal and ends the quarrel.

have been taken for something else by the present signal-receiver, just as the *Haplochromis* female regards the anal fin-spots as eggs, the male long-horned bee regards the orchis flowers as females and the bird takes the hover-fly to be a wasp. Probably quite a few signals have originally passed through a mimetic phase. It would therefore seem a promising method in some cases to test first whether nature has misused an existing response for a new function by imitating elsewhere the signal which primarily elicited this response and exaggerating it so that we are now more likely to notice the imitation than the model.

The investigation of mimicry has thus become an aid to the study

Figure 52. In baboons, females in oestrous produce a conspicuous signal in the form of a genital swelling, and this emphasises the pattern of invitation to copulation (presentation of the backside). This gesture further serves as a submissive display and as a greeting to belligerent and high-ranking group companions. In the hamadryas baboon (bottom), the males (right) have developed an imitation of the female oestrous swelling (left) to support this greeting display.
Top: backsides of the brown baboon *Papio anubis*, with the male on the left and the oestrous female on the right.

of the phylogeny of signals. Studies of mimicry will probably become just as important for this purpose as they are for their own sake. As explained above, we can really learn the truth about the evolution of signals best from the liars.

18 What is mimicry?

One can see from the examples just mentioned that mimicry is a very important field of research into evolution. Examples of mimicry have been used to illustrate evolution, and particularly adaptation, in many text-books, for example by Wallace and Srb. One reason for this is that it is easy to see the evolutionary direction, while in some cases it is even known how selection operates, namely in those cases where man has carried out artificial breeding, as discussed in the chapter on mimetic weeds. Although the mimetic effect is unintentional in such cases, there is one case of deliberate mimetic breeding by man. The Finnish bird-dog was bred for centuries to look like a fox so that it could be used as a dummy fox in hunting and deceiving birds; the dog now looks deceptively like a fox.

Mimicry can have various functions, one of which is protection. One cannot expect the protection to be absolute. Even genuine warning patterns do not frighten off certain predators, and these can then exploit this food-source without competition and may even eat the mimic as a bonus. The development of mimetic patterns is often accompanied by other changes, such as behaviour. One conspicuous feature, discovered independently by various investigators, is the greater resilience of many models as compared to their mimics. It is, of course, advantageous for a protected individual with warning coloration if it can withstand attacks from predators and thus benefit from its warning pattern. Some soft-skinned beetles of the family Lycidae run on unperturbed after being pecked at by three chickens. The well-known American monarch butterfly *Danaus plexippus*, which acts as a model for other butterflies, has very tough wings and scales, and can stand being held, whereas the scales of the unprotected mimics easily rub off when the wing is seized.

Blest made one interesting prediction, which he could only partially confirm. Many insects reproduce only once. If cryptically coloured palatable insects survive for some time after reproduction they increase the danger of discovery and thus the risk of acquainting the predator with the cryptic pattern. On the other hand with protected insects with warning coloration exactly the opposite applies. The longer these survive after reproduction the easier it is for predators to experience the unpleasant effects without damaging the species. The period of survival following reproduction should therefore be much shorter in cryptic, palatable insects than in protected insects with warning coloration.

Mimicry serves to deceive a signal-receiver. As a rule, deceptions are successful if they deceive at least once, though the more the better. Deceptive flowers, however, are only successful when they deceive the attracted animal twice. Once is not enough because the pollen must be collected from one site and taken to another. One would therefore expect these plants to handle their messengers carefully, and this is convincingly demonstrated by the pitcher-trap flowers of *Arisaema*, a member of the cuckoo-pint family. This plant has separate male and female inflorescences. Fungus gnats, which are attracted by the smell of ozone, tumble into the pitcher, fall past the male flower collecting pollen on the way, and then escape through an outlet at the base of the leaf. The female inflorescence is almost identical, except that it lacks an escape outlet so that the pollen-carriers are trapped and die. The escape outlet in the male inflorescence is an obvious adaptation which permits the messenger to visit another flower. Many *Stapelia* flowers are amazingly ruthless, for they have an odour so similar to that of carrion that carrion flies lay their eggs or larvae in them, and these then die. If this flower occurred in large numbers, it would wipe out its own pollen-carriers, but the plant occurs singly in desert areas.

One has to agree with critics of mimicry that the responses of the animals concerned are still poorly understood. Even so, believers in mimicry differ from the critics, particularly from their most voluble member Heikertinger, in believing that more detailed investigations often provide additional arguments in support of mimicry. These investigations cover all sorts of subsidiary aspects. Daumer, for example, investigated the appearance of flower colours to the bees themselves. Widely different animals were tested to determine how rapidly the response to an initial stimulus must be followed by a punishment stimulus in order for it to form a stable memory. The optimum interval is about half a second for many animals, while it lasts two seconds for a toothed carp. Sexton and others investigated the extent to which lizards would avoid unpalatable beetles with warning coloration even when they were hungry.

The learning capacity of the deceived animals plays an extremely variable role. Many deceived animals have no opportunity to learn since they are eaten, for example, by an angler fish, while others have extensive opportunities to learn, as in the case of the cleaning customers. The latter exert a strong selective pressure upon detailed imitation. Many warning colours are intended to be learned at the earliest opportunity and this also applies to other warning stimuli. Spiders avoid the malodorous leaf-bugs (Capsidae) after a single experience, though it is not known how long the effect persists. Furthermore, each warning or punishing stimulus affects only particular predators. For example, repulsive odours do not affect birds, while the defensive secretion ejected by the South American stick-insect *Anisomorpha* operates against ants, tiger-beetles, and jays but not against the opossum. Investigations of this kind in specific cases are still rare.

As already mentioned, mimetic characters need not necessarily exist to deceive a signal-receiver, and the same applies to non-deceptive signals. Anthocyanin colours in flowers attract insects, but the same substances occur in the leaves, stems and roots, and also in grasses and ferns, where the insects find nothing and where insect visits are of no use to the plant. Characters, signals or substances do not necessarily have the same function today as at some previous time, and when they do have several functions, we do not always know which was the original. For example, the defensive secretion of some ants functions at the same time as an alarm signal for conspecifics, which then come to help. Soft-skinned beetles of the genus *Stenus* employ the defensive secretion discharged from the rear of the abdomen also for swimming when they fall on to water. The secretion alters the surface tension and the rupture of the water film propels the beetle rapidly forwards.

Many defensive substances of insects can also be found as secondary plant products, where they may possibly serve to protect the plant against grazing; in the catmint for example, the substance nepetalacton also acts as an insect repellent. There are, of course, characters which have been obviously developed for particular functions. The pitcher-trap flowers of *Ceropegia* must stand exactly vertical so that the insects tumble in, and they have special sense organs to ensure vertical orientation. One cannot maintain that mimetic characters are always secondarily developed as imitations of a pre-existing model; they may be pre-adapted.

Most features that are usually insisted on as constituting mimicry are applicable only in special cases. Mimetic signals are not necessarily false warning signals; they may be developed for predation, brood-care, copulation or for some other drive. Examples for all these have been provided, and all of these examples, except intraspecific mimicry, have already been referred to as mimicry in literature. However, none of the definitions of mimicry quoted at the beginning of this book cover all our cases. What, then, is mimicry? We have already discussed some of the criteria used for defining mimicry, and in all cases the key point is the deceived signal-receiver. From the point of view of the receiver, one could distinguish between camouflage and mimicry, although in both cases a living organism simulates another object. Imitation of inanimate objects, such as sand, has been referred to as mimesis, and imitation of objects of plant and animal origin have been termed phytomimesis and zoomimesis respectively. However, this approach immediately causes confusion, since imitation of living leaves is not greatly different from imitation of dead leaves. The requirement that the model should be inanimate was soon discarded and this then created the problem of whether cuckoo eggs belong in the category of zoomimesis or aggressive mimicry. If one views mimicry from the point of view of the signal-receiver, a difference exists: if a signal of interest to the signal-receiver is imitated, then this is a case of mimicry, whereas if the generally uninteresting background or substrate is imitated, then camouflage (or mimesis) is involved. The importance of the response of the signal-receiver for the functioning of a mimicry-system is demonstrated by some experiments conducted by De Ruiter. Insectivorous birds avoid geometrid caterpillars because of their similarity to small twigs. However, if more caterpillars than similar-looking twigs are presented in a cage, the bird soon comes across a caterpillar and eats it. The bird then searches for further caterpillars of the same kind, and finally tries out the twigs as well. The twigs are thus treated as caterpillar mimics and share the caterpillar's fate. It is only when caterpillars are as rare as they are in the wild, or rather where twigs are far more numerous, that the disappointed bird leaves both alone. This example illustrates camouflage which, however, can be theoretically treated in the same way as Batesian mimicry, as shown in the following paragraphs.

One condition of mimicry is the existence of two different signal-transmitters, S_1 and S_2, which transmit the same signal and have at least one signal-receiver, E, in common which reacts similarly to both. One signal-transmitter is called the model and the other the mimic, the entire set-up being a mimicry-system. When it is advantageous for the signal-receiver to direct its response to one of the two transmitters, a plus sign is used, and when disadvantageous a minus sign. $S_1 + E - S_2$. That means: if the two signals were distinguishable by the signal-receiver, individual experience or selection would lead to different responses, as in the case of the cleaner mimic, where experienced cleaning customers actually distinguish cleaner and mimic and respond differently to the two.

This provides us with an opportunity to determine which organism in a mimicry-system is the model and which is the mimic. Previously this question has always been decided casually, as if the answer were obvious. However, there is a definite statement that covers this: the mimic is that one of the two signal-transmitters to which the receiver directs a response which is not of advantage to the receiver itself. The response would be selected against if it were to be developed only for this particular signal-transmitter. The response of the receiver is of course always advantageous as far as the mimic is concerned; otherwise the mimetic signal would not be preserved. If we agree to call the mimic S_2, the formula can be expanded into S_1 +E− +S_2.

In contrast to a widely held, largely intuitive opinion, the model S_1 need not necessarily benefit from the receiver's response. A mutual interest is present between model and receiver in cases of Peckhammian mimicry, where the model and receiver belong to the same species, and in cases of Batesian mimicry provided that the model is a living organism. An insect which is protected and possesses warning coloration naturally benefits if it is left alone by predators. On the other hand, it is definitely disadvantageous for a water-flea to be eaten by a fish, but it nevertheless serves as a model for trematode larvae which need to be swallowed. In a case of genuine Müllerian mimicry, all the animals concerned benefit: S_1+ +E+ +S_2. According to our definition, this is not mimicry since no agent is deceived and no difference exists between model and mimic. Attempts have been made to call a Müllerian mimic a transmitter that has secondarily developed similarities to another animal with warning coloration. This is difficult to establish, however, and little is gained because one could assume that both signal-transmitters have developed convergently and have reached a compromise, thus leaving us with two mimics and no model.

Yet another argument which is frequently introduced is the concept that in mimicry one species exploits another, which means that model and mimic must belong to separate species. Thus, when only one of two very closely related forms with warning coloration is protected, the decision whether mimicry is involved is left to the taxonomist. He must decide, for example, whether two species or two races are involved. It could of course be a polymorphic species with a defensive caste, as with soldier castes of ants and termites, in which case one could not use the term mimicry. This problem does in fact occur: in bees, wasps, and bumble-bees, the males are very similar to the females in appearance, but only the females are protected, largely by the evil-tasting sting poison, as Liepelt demonstrated. If one wished to adhere to the suggested criterion, one would be able to talk of mimicry when the males of one species are regarded as mimics of females of another species, but not when females of the same species are regarded as the models. This looks very artificial and so one has to admit the existence of intraspecific mimicry. Basically, such difficulties are dependent upon the assumption that the mimic must have developed its similarity independently. However, as discussed on page 83, this is by no means always the case. Common to all examples of mimicry which have been discussed is the deception of the signal-receiver by a counterfeit signal that carries a quite specific meaning for the receiver. This applies equally to intraspecific mimicry, since the individual concerned is deceived even when the deception is beneficial to the species, as explained for mouth-brooders.

Furthermore, it is important to know whether recognition of the significance of the signal is an innate or learned feature of the signal-receiver. Since all the cases so far investigated show that signal-receivers do not learn from one another, we can restrict our attention to learning from the object. 'E' in the formula stands for the individual, if the meaning of the signal is learned, and for the species if it is inherited. The distinction between model and mimic can be influenced by discovering whether the signal-receiver has to learn the signal or not. This is most obvious in cases of Mertensian mimicry. If the recognition of the coral snake pattern as a warning coloration is innate, the most poisonous representatives are the models, since they kill all predators which attack them. In simple terms, mutants which avoid objects with such coloration survive, and one can say that the species, so to speak, has learnt in developing this adaptation. However, if avoidance of the coral pattern is not an inherited feature but must be acquired by each through experience, the most poisonous forms must be mimics, since they offer the predator no chance to learn. In this case, the formula has the same form as that given above for Müllerian mimicry, although we can recognise one signal-transmitter as mimic. The formula presupposes that similar conditions exist on either side of the E. If the signal-receiver must first gain experience, but can only do this with one of the two transmitters, then the other thus becomes the mimic, even when the response directed towards the latter is advantageous to the signal-receiver. It should be kept in mind that this formula is a short-hand description for the sum of arguments which in most cases lead to the intuitive recognition of the model.

These considerations serve to demonstrate that it is important when interpreting cases of mimicry to have an exact knowledge of the signal-receiver and its responses to the signal. They also demonstrate the insight into the evolution of signals which can be gained from investigating suitable cases of mimicry. The examples in this book and the distinction between various forms of mimicry, such as Batesian, Peckhammian, Mertensian, show that one should not rely upon the original definitions that were based on the concept of false warning coloration and on the presence of a predator as signal-receiver. Transitional stages between mimicry and camouflage or between mimicry and the general standardisation of signals show that mimicry is not a principle distinct from the normal range of natural phenomena. The abundance of widely varying examples supports Henry Bates in his statement of 1862:

> The process by which a mimetic analogy is brought about in nature is a problem which involves that of the origin of all species and all adaptations.

Bibliography

Annandale, N., 'Observations on the habits and natural surroundings of insects made during the "Skeat Expedition" to the Malay Peninsula', 1899–1900, *Proc. Zool. Soc. Lond.* 837–69 (1900).

Baerends, G.P., 'The ethological analysis of incubation behaviour', *Ibis* **101**, 357–68 (1959).

—'La reconnaisance de l'oeuf par le Goéland argenté', *Bull. Soc. Sci. Bretagne*. **37**, 193–208 (1962).

Bänsch, R., 'Vegleichende Untersuchungen zur Biologie und zum Beutefangverhalten aphidivorer Coccinelliden, Chrysopiden und Syrphiden', *Zool. Jb. Syst.* **91**, 271–340 (1964).

Beebe, W.A., 'Contribution to the life history of the Euchromid moth, *Aethria carnicauda* Butler', *Zoologica*, N.Y. **38**, 155–60 (1953).

Blest, A.D., 'The function of eyespot patterns in the Lepidoptera', *Behaviour* **11**, 209–56 (1957).

— 'Longevity, palatability and natural selection in five species of New World Saturniid moth', *Nature, Lond.* **197**, 1183–86 (1963).

Brower, J.v.Z., 'Experimental studies of Mimicry 4', *Amer. Nat* **44**, 271–82 (1960).

Brower, L.P. and J.v.Z., and Collins, C.T., 'Experimental studies of Mimicry 7', *Zoologica, N.Y.* **48**, 65–84 (1963).

Brower, J.v.Z. and L.P., 'Experimental studies of Mimicry 8', *Amer. Nat.* **49**, 173–88 (1965).

Brower, L.P. and J.v.Z., and Cranston, F.P., 'Courtship behaviour of the Queen Butterfly, *Danaus gilippus berenice* Cramer', *Zoologica, N.Y.*, **50**, 1–39 (1965).

Burns, J.M., 'Preferential mating versus Mimicry', *Science* **153**, 551–53 (1966).

China, W.E., 'Historical survey of notes on the "protective" resemblance to a spike of blossom borne by clusters of an African Homopteran of the genus *Ityraea*', *Ann. Mag. Nat. Hist.* **10**, (3), 347–54 (1929).

Clarke, C.A., and Sheppard, P.M., 'Interactions between major genes and polygenes in the determination of the mimetic patterns of *Papilio dardanus*', *Evolution* **17**, 404–13 (1963).

Cowgill, U.M., '*Perodicticus potto* and some insects', *J. Mammal.* **47**, 156–57 (1966).

Crane, J., 'Imaginal behavior of a Trinidad butterfly, *Heliconius erato hydara* Hewitson, with special reference to the social use of color', *Zoologica, N.Y.* **40**, 167–96 (1955).

Curio, E., 'Die Schutzanpassungen dreier Raupen eines Schwärmers

(Lepidopt., Sphingidae) auf Galapagos, *Zool. Jb. Syst.* **92**, 487–522 (1965).
Curio, E., 'Ein Falter mit "falchem Kopf" ', *Natur und Museum* **95**, 43–6 (1965).
Darlington, P.J., 'Experiments on Mimicry in Cuba, with suggestions for future study', *Trans. Roy. Entomol. Soc. London* **87**, 681–95 (1938).
Daumer, K., 'Blumenfarben, wie die Bienen sie sehen', *Z. vergl. Physiol.* **41**, 49–110 (1958).
Duncan, C.J., and Sheppard, P.M., 'Sensory discrimination and its role in the evolution of Batesian Mimicry', *Behaviour* **24**, 269–82 (1965).
Eisner, T., Kafatos, F.C., and Linsley, E.G., 'Lycid predation by mimetic adult Cerambycidae (Coleoptera)', *Evolution* **16**, 316–24 (1962).
Eisner, T., and Shepherd, J., 'Caterpillar feeding on a sundew plant', *Science* **150**, 1608–09 (1965).
Eisner, T., and Meinwald, J., 'Defensive secretions of arthropods', *Science* **153**, 1341–50 (1966).
Feder, H.M., 'Cleaning symbiosis in the marine environment', Henry, S.M., (ed.) *Symbiosis*, Vol I, Academic Press, New York and London, 327–80, 1966.
Ford, E.B., *Ecological Genetics*, London and New York, 1964.
Gatenby, J.B., 'The New Zealand glow-worm', *Tuatara* **8**, 86–92 (1960).
Gertsch, W.J., 'Spiders that lasso their prey', *Natural History* **56**, 152–58 (Mag. Am. Mus. Nat. Hist.) (1947).
Gilbert, J.J., 'Rotifer ecology and embryological induction', *Science* **151**, 1234–37 (1966).
Hall, B.P., Moreau, R.E., and Galbraith, I.C.J., 'Polymorphism and parallelism in the African bush-shrikes of the genus *Malaconotus*', *Ibis* **108**, 161–182 (1966).
Heikertinger, F., *Das Rätsel der Mimikry und seine Lösung*, Jena, 1954.
Herrebout, W.M., Kuyten, P.J., and Ruiter, L.de, 'Observations on color patterns and behaviour of caterpillars feeding on Scots Pine', *Arch. néerl. Zool.* **15**, 315–57 (1963).
Hinde, S.L., 'The protective resemblance to flowers borne by an African homopterous insect, *Flata nigrocincta, Trans. Ent. Soc. Lond.* (IV), 695–98 (1902).
Hingston, R.W.G., 'Protective devices in spiders' snares', *Proc. Zool. Soc. Lond.* (1927).
Hocking, B., and Sharplin, C.D., 'Flower basking by arctic insect'. *Nature, Lond.*, **208**, 215 (1965).
Hohorst, W., and Graefe, G., 'Ameisen – obligatorische Zwischenwirte des

Lanzettegels (*Dicrocoelium dendriticum*)', *Naturwiss.* **48**, 229–30 (1961).
Hull, C. L., *Principles of Behavior*, New York, 1943.
Kettlewell, H. B. D., 'Insect adaptations', *Animals* **5**, 520–23 (1965).
Kinsley, E. G., Mimetic form and coloration in the Cerambicidae (Coleoptera), *Ann. Entomol. Soc. Amer.* **52**, 125–31 (1958).
Kloft, W., 'Versuch einer Analyse der trophobiotischen Beziehungen von Ameisen zu Aphiden', *Biol. Zbl.* **78**, 863–70 (1959).
Kügler, H., 'Uber die optische Wirkung von Fliegenblumen auf Fliegen', *Ber. dtsch. Botan. Ges.* **69**, 387–98 (1956).
— *Einführung in die Blütenökologie*, Stuttgart, 1966.
Kullenberg, B., 'Studies in *Ophrys* pollination', *Zool. Bidrag Uppsala* **34**, 1–340 (1961).
Kuyten, P., 'Verhaltensbeobachtungen an der Raupe des Kaiseratlas', *Entomol. Z.* **72**, 203–7 (1962).
Lane, C., and Rothschild, M., 'A case of Müllerian Mimicry of sound', *Proc. Roy. Ent. Soc. London* (A) **40**, 156–8 (1965).
Liepelt, W., 'Zur Schutzwirkung des Stachelgiftes von Bienen und Wespen gegenüber Trauerfliegenschnäpper und Fartenrotschwanz', *Zool. Jb. Physiol.* **70**, 167–76 (1963).
Linsley, E. G., Eisner, T., and Klots, A. B., 'Mimetic assemblages of sibling species of lycid beetles', *Evolution* **15**, 15–29 (1961).
Lloyd, J. E., 'Aggressive Mimicry in *Photuris*: Firefly femmes fatales', *Science* **149**, 653–4 (1965).
Magnus, D., 'Experimentelle Untersuchungen zur Bionomie und Ethologie des Kaisermantels *Argynnis paphia* L. *Z. Tierpsychol.* **15**, 397–426 (1958).
Matthes, D., 'Excitatoren und Paarungsverhalten mitteleuropäischer Malachiiden (Coleopt., Malacodermata)', *Z. Morph. Ökol. Tiere* **51**, 375–546 (1962).
Meeuse, B. J. D., *The story of Pollination*, New York, 1961.
— '*The Voodoo Lily*,' *Sci. Amer.* **215**, (1), 80–8 (1966).
Mertens, R., 'Die Warn- und Droh-Reaktionen der Reptilien', *Abh. Senckenberg. naturf. Ges. No. 471* (Frankfurt/Main) (1946).
— 'Das Problem der Mimikry bei Korallenschlangen', *Zool. Jb. Syst.* **84**, 541–76 (1966).
— *The World of Amphibians and Reptiles*, London, 1960.
Mothes, K., 'Zur Problematik der metabolischen Exkretion bei Pflanzen', *Naturwiss.* **53**, 317–23 (1966).
Nelson, K., 'Behaviour and morphology in the glandulocaudine fishes', *Univ. California Publ. Zool.* **75**, 59–152 (1964).

Ottow, J., and Duve, G., 'Zur Kenntnis der Fortplanzung von *Chrysococcyx caprius* und *Cuculus canorus gularis* in Süd-Afrika', *J. Ornith.* **106**, 431–39 (1965).
Owen, D.F., 'Industrial melanism in North American moths', *Amer. Nat.* **95**, 227–33 (1961).
— 'Similar polymorphismus in an insect and a land snail', *Nature, Lond.* **198**, 201–3 (1963).
Palen, G.F., and Goddard, F.V., 'Catnip and oestrous behaviour in the cat', *Anim. Behav.* **14,** 372–77 (1966).
Pocock, R.I., 'Warning coloration in the musteline carnivora', *Proc. Zool. Soc. Lond.* 944–59 (1908).
Poulsen, H., 'A study of incubation responses and some other behaviour patterns in birds', *Videsnk. Medd. fra Dansk. naturh. Foren* **115**, 1–131 (1953).
Punnet, R.C., *Mimicry in Butterflies*, Cambridge, 1915.
Randall, J.E. and H.E., 'Examples of Mimicry and protective resemblance in tropical marine fishes', *Bull. Mar. Sci. Gulf & Caribbean* **10**, 444–80 (1960).
Rick, C.M., and Bowman, R.I., 'Galapagos tomatoes and tortoises', *Evolution* **15**, 407–17 (1961).
Robinson, J., *Pilobolus* spp. and the translation of the infective larvae of a *Dictyocaulus viviparus* from faeces to pastures, *Nature, Lond.* **193**, 353 (1962).
Rothschild, M., 'Fleas', *Sci. Amer.* **312**, 44–53 (1965).
Ruiter, L.de., 'Some remarks on problems of the ecology and evolution of Mimicry', *Arch. Néerl. Zool.* **13**, 1. Suppl., 351–68 (1958).
Schifter, H., 'Beobachtungen am Grossmaulwels *Chaca chaca*', *Natur und Museum* **95**, 465–72 (1965).
Schremmer. F., 'Wechselbeziehungen zwischen Pilzen und Insekten', *österr. Bot. Z.* **110**, 380–400 (1963).
Schwalb, H.H., 'Beiträge zur Biologie der einheimischen Lampyriden', *Zool. Jb. Syst.* **88**, 399–550 (1961).
Seevers, C.H., 'The systematics, evolution and zoogeography of Staphylinid beetles associated with army ants (Coleoptera, Staphylinidae)', *Fieldiana, Zoology* **47**, 137–351 (1965).
Sexton, O.J., Hoger, C., and Ortleb, E., '*Anolis carolinensis*: Effects of feeding on reaction to aposematic prey', *Science* **153**, 1140 (1966).
Sharp, D., 'The modification and attitude of *Idolum diabolicum*, a Mantis of the kind called "floral simulators"', *Proc. Cambr. Philos. Soc.* **10**, 175–180 (1899).
Shelford, R., 'Observations on some mimetic insects and spiders from

Borneo and Singapore', *Proc. Zool. Soc. Lond.* 230–74 (Pt. 2) (1902).
— 'Mimicry amongst the Blattidae; with a revision of the genus *Prosoplecta* Sauss., and the description of a new genus', *Proc. Zool. Soc. Lond.* 358–76 (1919).
Sibley, C.S., 'Behavioral Mimicry in titmice (Paridae) and certain other birds', *The Wilson Bull.* **67**, 128–32 (1955).
Stride, G.O., 'Investigations into the courtship behaviour of the male of *Hypolimnas misippus* L. (Lepidoptera, Nymphalidae), with special reference to the role of visual stimuli', *Brit. J. anim. Beh.* **5**, 153–67 (1957)
— 'Further studies on the courtship behaviour of African mimetic butterflies', *Brit. J. anim. Beh.* **6**, 224–30 (1958).
Szidat, L., 'Uber cysticerke Riesencercarien', *Z. f. Parasitenkde.* **4** 477–505 (1932).
Turner, J.G.F., 'Evolution of complex polymorphism and Mimicry in distasteful South American butterflies', *Proc. 13th Congr. Entomol. Lond.* **4**, 267 (1965).
Vogel, S., 'Duftdrüsen im Dienste der Bestäubung. Uber Bau und Funktion der Osmophoren', *Abh. Akad. Wies. Lit. Mainz* (math. -nat. Reihe) Nr. 10 (1963).
— 'Pollination neotropischer Orchideen durch duftstoff-höselnde Prachtbienen-Männchen', *Naturwiss.* **53**, 181–2 (1966).
Wallace, B. and Srb, A.M., 'Adaptation' (2nd ed.), 1964.
Wasman, E., 'Die Ameisenmimikry', *Abhandl. z. theoret. Biol.* **19**, (1925).
Wickler, W., 'Zur Stammesgeschichte funcktionell korrelierte Organ- und Verhaltensmerkmale: Ei-Attrappen und Maulbrüten bei afrikanischen Cichliden'. *Z. Tierpsychol.* **19**, 129–64 (1962).
— 'Zum Problem der Signalbildung, am Beispiel der Verhaltensmimikry zwischen *Aspidontus* und *Labroides*', *Z. Tierpsychol.* **20**, 657–79 (1963).
— 'Mimicry and the evolution of animal communication', *Nature, Lond.* **208**, 519–21 (1966).
— 'Socio-sexual signals and their intraspecific imitation among primates', Morris, D., (ed.) *Primate Ethology*, London.
Wiesmann, R., 'Geruchsorientierung der Stubenfliege *Musca domestica* L.', *Z. angew. Entomol.* **50**, 74–81 (1962).
Willis, E.O., 'Is the zone-tailed hawk a mimic of the turkey vulture?' *The Condor* **65**, 313–17 (1963).
Wynne-Edwards, V.C., *Animal Dispersion in Relation to Behaviour*, Edinburgh and London, 1962.

Films

Some of the behavioural observations discussed in this book are recorded in documentary films, which have been published by the *Institut für den wissenschaftlichen Film* (34 Göttingen, Nonnenstieg 72, Germany). These films can be obtained on loan from this organisation.
All E-films can be obtained through the following agencies:
Austria: Bundesstaatliche Hauptstelle für Lichtbild und Bildungsfilm, Sensengasse 3, Vienna IX.
Holland: Stichting Film en Wetenschap, Universitaire Film, Catharijnesingel 59, Utrecht.
USA: Pennsylvania State University, 103 Carnegie Building, University Park, Pennsylvania 16802.
(Titles translated):
Optical recognition of females in butterflies: 'Visual schema "female" in the mother-of-pearl butterfly (experiments with models)' W 705
Cryptic and protective patterns:
'*Maja verrucosa* (Majidae) – Crypsis' E 894
'Protective coloration and protective patterns in insects' C 264
Defensive behaviour in caterpillars:
'*Dicranura vinula* (Notodontidae) – threat behaviour' E 973
Predatory behaviour in Angler-fish:
'*Antennarius nummifer* (Antennariidae) – prey-catching' E 141
'*Phrynelox scaber* (Antennariidae) – prey-catching' E 1039
Trematode sporocysts in snails:
'*Leucochloridium macrostomum* (Trematodes) – sporocyst stage in *Succinea putris* and *Succinea elegans* (Succineidae)' E 634
Carnivorous plants: 'Sensitivity and performance of the animal-trap apparatus of *Dionaea muscipula* (Venus fly-trap)' C 333
Ejection of nest-companions by the cuckoo:
'The innate responses of the nestling cuckoo' C 385
Behaviour of the cleaner wrasse and its mimic:
'*Labroides dimidiatus* (Labridae) – cleaning of various fish. Under-water film sequences.' E 754
'*Labroides dimidiatus* (Labridae) – cleaning of various fish. Aquarium film sequences.' E 127
'*Aspidontus taeniatus* (Blenniidae) – feeding behaviour.' E 140
'*Runula rhinorhynchus* (Blenniidae) – feeding behaviour' E 139
Spawning in mouth-brooding Cichlids with egg-dummies:
'*Haplochromis burtoni* (Cichlidae) – spawning' E 1122
'*Haplochromis wingatii* (Cichlidae) – courtship and spawning' E 523

Subject index

Numerals in bold refer to captions, illustrations, or both

Species index

World University Library

Already published

001 **Eye and Brain**
R. L. Gregory, *Edinburgh*

002 **The Economics of Underdeveloped Countries**
Jagdish Bhagwati, *MIT*

003 **The Left in Europe since 1789**
David Caute, *Oxford*

004 **The World Cities**
Peter Hall, *London*

005 **Chinese Communism**
Robert North, *Stanford*

006 **The Emergence of Greek Democracy**
W. G. Forrest, *Oxford*

007 **The Quest for Absolute Zero**
K. Mendelssohn, *Oxford*

008 **The Biology of Work**
O. G. Edholm, *London*

009 **Palaeolithic Cave Art**
P. J. Ucko and A. Rosenfeld, *London*

010 **Particles and Accelerators**
R. Gouiran, *C E R N*

011 **Russian Writers and Society 1825–1904**
Ronald Hingley, *Oxford*

012 **Words and Waves**
A. H. W. Beck, *Cambridge*

013 **Education in the Modern World**
John Vaizey, *Oxford*

014 **The Rise of Toleration**
Henry Kamen, *Warwick*

015 **Art Nouveau**
S. Tschudi Madsen, *Oslo*

016 **The World of an Insect**
Rémy Chauvin, *Strasbourg*

017 **Decisive Forces in World Economics**
J. L. Sampedro, *Madrid*

018 **Development Planning**
Jan Tinbergen, *Rotterdam*

019 **Human Communication**
J. L. Aranguren, *Madrid*

020 **Mathematics Observed**
Hans Freudenthal, *Utrecht*

021 **The Rise of the Working Class**
Jürgen Kuczynski, *Berlin*

022 **The Science of Decision-making**
A. Kaufmann, *Paris*

023 **Chinese Medicine**
P. Huard and M. Wong, *Paris*

024 **Muhammad and the Conquests of Islam**
Francesco Gabrieli, *Rome*

025 **Humanism in the Renaissance**
S. Dresden, *Leyden*

026 **What is Light?**
A. C. S. van Heel and C. H. F. Velzel, *Eindhoven*

027 **Bionics**
Lucien Gérardin, *Paris*

028 **The Age of the Dinosaurs**
Björn Kurtén, *Helsingfors*

029 **Mimicry**
Wolfgang Wickler, *Seewiesen*

030 **The Old Stone Age**
François Bordes, *Bordeaux*